THE ULTIMATE HISTORY BUFF CHALLENGE

OVER 600 QUIZ QUESTIONS
FOR CURIOUS HISTORY LOVERS

BILL O'NEILL

CONTENTS

DON'T FORGET:
TWO FREE BOOKS

INTRODUCTION

How much do you know about history?

Could you name, say, the country where The Peasant's Revolt took place way back in 1381? Do you know which of Christopher Columbus' three ships sank when it struck a reef off the coast of Haiti in 1492? Could you name the famous Roman leader who switched allegiances only to commit suicide in Egypt in 30 BCE? And do you know which of Henry VIII's six wives not only outlived England's most notorious king but married someone else - her fourth husband, no less! Also, it was only six months after his death.

If questions like these have you shouting out answers, scratching your head, or even boggling your mind trying to come up with the solution, then this is the book for you!

This is *The Ultimate History Buff Challenge*- a compendium of more than 600 fiendish history questions specially compiled to test your knowledge of the past to its limits. What follows are 34 quizzes, each containing more than a dozen questions dedicated to a different historical period or topic — from Ancient Egypt and Ancient Greece right through the political scandals and upheavals of the 20th century.

The chapters here have been arranged in roughly chronological order, moving forward through time, covering around 5,000 years of history from start to finish. The quizzes themselves, meanwhile, contain a tricky mixture of multiple-choice, true, or false, and standard quiz questions. Not to worry if you get stuck, though - there are full solutions (along with some much-needed background information and extra details) at the end of each quiz. With that in mind, keep an eye out for some extra fascinating facts and bonus trivia along the way as well!

So, let's get started! First, we're heading the furthest back in time we'll go in this book, to a time when the pharaohs of Ancient Egypt ruled over what was then perhaps the most powerful empire the world had ever seen...

1.
EGYPT & THE EGYPTIANS

More than 5,000 years ago - sometime in the late 4th millennium BCE, around 3100 BCE - a grand ruler of Northeast Africa named 'Menes the Great' brought together the two vast regions of Upper and Lower Egypt as a single kingdom under his control.

The realm that Menes created would form the basis of what we now know as Ancient Egypt. For the next 3,000 years, a series of grand kings and queens, known as pharaohs, would rule over this vast region of North Africa creating one of the largest, most powerful, and most successful empires the world has ever seen. From agriculture to architecture, music to medicine, and language to technology, the Ancient Egyptians pioneered almost every aspect of the modern world - while leaving behind some of our most extraordinary buildings and artifacts. But how much do you *really* know about this most remarkable period of ancient history and its people and places?

1. Ra was the Ancient Egyptian god of the sun. He was usually portrayed with the head of what creature?

    a. Lion
    b. Crocodile
    c. Falcon
    d. Ibis

2. True or false: In total, the Egyptians worshipped more than 1,000 different gods and goddesses.

3. In Ancient Egypt, what would be kept in vessels called Coptic jars?

    a. Honey
    b. Water
    c. Bodily organs
    d. Bitumen

4. Also known as Cheops, the largest of the Egyptian pyramids - the Great Pyramid of Giza- is the tomb of which ancient ruler?

    a. Rameses
    b. Khufu
    c. Nefertiti
    d. Thutmose

5. Papyrus was the Ancient Egyptians' equivalent of paper. But what was it made from?

   a. Animal hide
   b. Fabric
   c. Clay
   d. Plants

6. In Egyptian mythology, who was the sister (and in some traditions, the wife) of the god Osiris?

   a. Horus
   b. Isis
   c. Hathor
   d. Sekhmet

7. What would someone in Ancient Egypt do with something called senet?

   a. Play it
   b. Eat it
   c. Wear it
   d. Drink it

8. Which of these cities was NOT at any point the capital of Ancient Egypt?

   a. Aswan
   b. Alexandria
   c. Thebes
   d. Memphis

9. He might be the most famous of all the pharaohs, but King Tutankhamun was surprisingly short-lived. How old was he when he died (in mysterious circumstances) in 1323 BCE?

   a. 9
   b. 15
   c. 20
   d. 31

10. Pharaoh Ramses II lived for over 90 years and ruled Egypt for more than 60 - yet he only ever fathered one son. Is that true or false?

11. It might have been the title of an Egyptian ruler, but what does the word pharaoh mean?

   a. Great house
   b. Great head
   c. Great heart
   d. Great help

12. Perhaps to make herself appear more powerful in royal documents, one of Egypt's most important female pharaohs, Hatshepsut, is believed to have requested she be portrayed in pictures of herself…?

   a. …riding a lion
   b. …holding an axe in both hands
   c. …far taller than everyone else around her
   d. …with a man's beard and hairy chest

13. In 525 BCE, the Egyptian Empire was conquered by one of its neighbors. Which equally ancient civilization took over?

   a. The Berbers
   b. The Carthaginians
   c. The Persians
   d. The Nubians

14. Some historians believe the Egyptians used a mixture of myrrh oil, ground ox bones, eggshells, and water as an early kind of what?

   a. Makeup
   b. Toothpaste
   c. Ink
   d. Paint

15. Much of the Ancient Egyptian calendar centered around something that happened to the River Nile every September. What was it?

16. In what year was King Tutankhamun's tomb discovered in Egypt by the archaeologist Howard Carter?

   a. 1888
   b. 1902
   c. 1922
   d. 1944

17. According to legend, what kind of snake did Queen Cleopatra use to commit suicide?

   a. Asp
   b. Mamba
   c. Boa
   d. Adder

18. If you were to unwrap the bandages on a typical Egyptian mummy, how long would they be?

   a. 219 yards
   b. 820 yards
   c. 1203 yards
   d. 1531 yards

SOLUTIONS

1. C. Falcon. According to some versions of his mythology, Ra swept across the sky as a bird during the daytime.
2. True! In fact, the actual figure is likely closer to 1,500 - although if the deities historians don't know the names or full details of are included, the total figure is perhaps more than 2,000!
3. C. Bodily organs. When a person's body was mummified in Ancient Egypt, some of their vital organs - including the brain and heart - were often removed and stored beside the body in so-called Coptic jars, in preparation for the afterlife.
4. B. Khufu. The second pharaoh of Egypt's Fourth Dynasty, Pharaoh Khufu is thought to have commissioned the Great Pyramid sometime in the early 26th century BCE.
5. D. Plants. Papyrus is made from the woody pith of the papyrus plant, which is a kind of reed-like sedge that grows along the Nile.
6. B. Isis.
7. A. Play it. Senet was a board game popular in Egypt for over 2,000 years.
8. A. Aswan. The capital of Ancient Egypt changed some 18 times throughout the empire's long history, until Cairo was finally chosen in the late 10th century. At no point in all those years, however, did the modern city of Aswan ever hold the title of capital; Memphis, on the other hand, was Ancient Egypt's longest-serving capital and held the position for more than 700 years.
9. C. 20. Mystery has long surrounded King Tut's death - with some Egyptologists believing that the injuries to his skeleton suggest he may even have been killed by a crocodile or a hippopotamus! Other historians believe he died of an infection in a wound.
10. False. Quite the opposite in fact: historians believe Ramses may have fathered around 60 to 100 children during his long life!
11. A. Great house. Probably as a reference to the grand palaces in which the pharaohs lived.
12. D. ...with a man's beard and hairy chest!
13. C. The Persians.
14. B. Toothpaste! Traces of this bizarre mixture - which often also included granules of pumice stone - have been found in Egyptian

vessels, leading some archaeologists and historians to believe the Egyptians used it to clean their teeth.

15. It flooded. It might sound like a disaster, but the annual flooding of the Nile in the early autumn refreshed the surrounding farmland and brought much-needed nutrients to the parched soil. In years when the floods failed, were delayed, or were too heavy, Egypt often suffered months of famine as a result.

16. C. 1922.

17. A. Asp. According to the Greek historian Plutarch, Cleopatra tested various deadly poisons and venoms on condemned prisoners in her jails. She decided that the bite of the asp - thought to be the name at the time of what we'd now call the Egyptian cobra - was the least terrible way to die.

18. D. 1531 yards. Typically, just under a mile of bandages was used in wrapping a mummy—though some have been found with more than one mile of wrappings!

DID YOU KNOW?

Ancient Egypt lasted so long - and Queen Cleopatra reigned so late in its history - that her lifetime is closer to ours today than to the building of the Pyramids!

2.
ANCIENT GREECE

While Egypt was flourishing on the north coast of Africa, on the opposite side of the Mediterranean an entirely new - but equally historically significant - culture was emerging.

What we know as Ancient Greece was for much of its history a loose collection of regions, nations, counties, and city-states, bound by various linguistic, cultural, and political ties. Many of these ancient regions and states - like Thessaly and Thrace - as well as the city-states or *poleis* they contained - like Sparta and Thebes - have gone on to be just as famous as the Greek world themselves, thanks to the famous individuals and events that took place there. And as these influential Greeks and Greek states grew in power and cultural importance, so too did the impact Ancient Greece had on the world at large: it is the Greeks, for instance, that we can credit with everything from geometry to modern philosophy, enormous advances in sciences like astronomy and physics, and even the foundational tenets of modern drama, architecture, and even democracy itself. Now let's test your knowledge of this incredible civilization!

1. The Ancient Greek mathematician and inventor Archimedes is famously said to have shouted "Eureka!" on his discovery of what basic principle?

    a. Gravity
    b. Optical refraction
    c. Water displacement
    d. Light dispersion

2. Which famous Greek ruler and military figure was the son of Philip II, king of Macedon?

    a. Pericles
    b. Leonidas
    c. Draco
    d. Alexander

3. The earliest record of what aspect of Greek culture dates from 776 BCE?

    a. Theatrical performance
    b. Consultation of an oracle
    c. The Olympic Games
    d. Worship of Zeus

4. One of the classical Seven Wonders of the Ancient World was located at Olympia in Ancient Greece. What was it?

   a. Statue
   b. Temple
   c. Lighthouse
   d. Library

5. The ancient Greek city of Naxos was founded on what Mediterranean island in 733 BCE?

   a. Corfu
   b. Cyprus
   c. Sicily
   d. Crete

6. The word draconian, meaning especially severe, is an allusion to an Ancient Greek figure named Draco. What did he become known in his day?

   a. Lawmaker
   b. Soldier
   c. Pirate
   d. Architect

7. What part of the famous Greek Acropolis at Athens is properly known as the *propylaea*?

   a. The roof
   b. The steps
   c. The pillars
   d. The gates

8. The famous Greek mathematician and philosopher Pythagoras was vegetarian. True or false?

9. The Greek island of Crete was once home to what ancient Bronze Age civilization?

   a. Minoa
   b. Sumer
   c. Kush
   d. Nubia

10. For what would a person in Ancient Greece have used a device called a *clepsydras*?

    a. To cook
    b. To fire arrows
    c. To tell the time
    d. To play music

11. Which of these is NOT widely held to be an invention of Archimedes?

    a. Catapult
    b. Pulley
    c. Screw pump
    d. Grappling hook

12. The Greek ruler Croesus, a king of Lydia, was known for his...what?

    a. Height
    b. Book collection
    c. Sleight of hand
    d. Wealth

13. When they took their alphabet from the nearby people of ancient Phoenicia, what did the Greeks add to it?

    a. Punctuation
    b. Upper and lowercase letters
    c. Vowels
    d. A standard A to Z order

14. True or false: The original ancient Greek Olympic athletes performed their sports wearing golden armor.

15. Which famous Greek philosopher and polymath was the personal tutor of Alexander the Great?

    a. Aristotle
    b. Plato
    c. Galen
    d. Zeno

16. Where did Socrates famously spend the final day of his life, aged 71?

    a. At sea
    b. Atop Mount Olympus

c. In a cave
d. In prison

17. What was a barbiton in Ancient Greece?

    a. A musical instrument
    b. A wine bottle
    c. A fishing boat
    d. A white robe

18. What was the Four Hundred, which took place in Athens in 411 BCE?

    a. A sea battle
    b. A sports competition
    c. A coup
    d. A banquet

SOLUTIONS

1. C. Water displacement. Archimedes is said to have noted that the level of the water in his bathtub rose when he sat in it, and in doing so discovered the standard principle that the volume of water displaced by a body submerged in water must be equal to its volume.
2. D. Alexander. Philip was the father of Alexander the Great, who succeeded him as King of Macedon in 336 BCE.
3. C. The Olympic Games. The first ancient Olympics were held in 776 BCE, and the last in CE 393E, under the emperor Theodosius the Great.
4. A. Statue. The Statue of Zeus at Olympia was a gigantic, seated figure of the Greek god Zeus made by a renowned sculptor named Phidias sometime around 435 BCE. The statue stood a colossal 41 feet tall!
5. C. Sicily. In the 730s BCE, a party of Greek citizens from the island of Euboea near Athens sailed across the Mediterranean to establish a new Greek city-state, Naxos, in what is now modern-day Italy.
6. A. Lawmaker. In the 7th century BCE, Draco introduced a new written system of Greek law - the Draconian constitution - replacing the orally circulated and mutually understood system that had existed before then. His laws were so severe, with many now punishable by death, that his name became an allusion to anything equally harsh or unyielding.
7. D. The gates. The purpose of the *propylaea* was a symbolic separation of the religious site of the Acropolis from the secular site of the rest of the city.
8. True. Pythagoras and all the followers of his school of philosophy were all strict vegetarians - with some writers of the time claiming he even went as far as to refuse to socialize with butchers, cooks, and hunters.
9. A. Minoa. The Minoan civilization is often said to have been the earliest civilization in modern Europe.
10. C. To tell the time. A *clepsydras* is a water clock.
11. A. Catapult. Archimedes' engineering and mathematical knowledge led to him inventing the compound pulley, the screw pump (also known as an Archimedes screw) for raising water, and a fiendish military device called an Archimedes claw, which used a vast grappling hook to life enemies' ships from the water.
12. D. Wealth. Hence the expression "as rich as Croesus."

13. C. Vowels. The Phoenician alphabet was already in a standard order, and both punctuation and upper and lowercase letters were much later developments. The Greeks, however, took a handful of the letters from the Phoenician alphabet that they didn't have an equivalent sound for in their own language, and used them to represent the basic Greek vowel sounds; the Phoenician alphabet, as it happens, had been a system called an abjad, in which only consonants are represented in writing.
14. False. In fact, they typically performed naked.
15. A. Aristotle.
16. D. In prison. In 399 BCE, Socrates was accused of corrupting the youth of Greece and sentenced to death. Despite his followers and students offering to aid his escape, he resigned himself to his fate and died in prison, having been forced to drink poisonous hemlock.
17. A. A musical instrument.
18. C. A coup. Following several years of financial problems and social unrest, the democratically elected government of Athens was overthrown in a rebellion in 411 BCE and replaced for a short time with a new "people's" government, or oligarchy, that became known as the Four Hundred. The group's coup - known as the Coup of the Four Hundred, or the Athenian coup of 411 BCE - was short-lived and within a matter of months was replaced by an even larger group, known as the Five Thousand, before democratic order was finally restored.

DID YOU KNOW?

The works of Aristotle were almost lost forever. After his death in 332 BCE, they were stored in a basement and forgotten about!

3.
THE ROMANS

When the Ancient Egyptian world came to an end with the death of Queen Cleopatra in 30 BCE, Egypt fell under the control of the Romans.

The origins of Ancient Rome are as long and complex - and are as wrapped in mystery and mythology as those of Ancient Egypt. In general, though, historians tend to see the rule of Emperor Octavian (also known as Augustus) beginning in 31 BCE as the start of what we would now call the Roman Empire.

For the next 400 years, the Romans would expand their territory over much of Europe, North Africa, and western Asia, eventually advancing as far north as the northernmost counties of England, as far west as Spain and Portugal, as far south as the Nile Valley, and as far east as the Caspian Sea.

The empire eventually became so great - and the Romans eventually took control over so many different peoples and nations - that civil war and near-constant uprisings and invasions plagued its later years.

The entire Roman Empire eventually split in two, forming opposing East and West regions, in 395 CE. And while the Western Roman Empire endured for another century or so, the Eastern or Byzantine Empire would not fall until as relatively recently as the mid-15th century!

Let's see how much of that vast history you know about with these trick questions all about Rome and the Romans...

1. Calpurnia was the wife of which famous Roman ruler?

    a. Nero
    b. Claudius
    c. Julius Caesar
    d. Marc Antony

2. 69 CE was a particularly tumultuous year in the history of the Roman Empire, which became known as The Year of the Four...?

    a. Emperors
    b. Wars
    c. Fires
    d. Floods

3. The month of August is famously named after the Roman emperor Augustus. But which other month of the year is named after a Roman emperor?

   a. January
   b. June
   c. July
   d. November

4. The name of the infamous Roman leader Caligula is thought to mean…?

   a. Little head
   b. Little boots
   c. Little hand
   d. Little luck

5. In Ancient Rome, what would an *auspex* have done?

   a. Fought in the army
   b. Cooked the emperor's meals
   c. Made boats
   d. Predicted the future

6. True or false. Julius Caesar was born by Caesarian section, hence this remarkable emergency obstetric procedure's name.

7. Which of these things did the Emperor Nero NOT do?

   a. Have his mother murdered
   b. Have his wife murdered
   c. Marry his favorite male slave
   d. Marry his daughter

8. Which famous Roman is said to have discovered the (now lost) tomb of Archimedes?

   a. Cicero
   b. Pliny the Elder
   c. Marc Antony
   d. Plutarch

9. What was Quintus Horatius Flaccus better known as Horace - famed as in the Ancient Roman world?

a. Poet

b. Architect

c. Mathematician

d. Gladiator

10. Who was the stepson, former son-in-law, and adopted son of Emperor Augustus, who succeeded him as Rome's second emperor in 14 CE?

a. Trajan

b. Tiberius

c. Titus

d. Tacitus

11. Which famous Roman emperor is thought by some historians to have never consummated his marriage to his wife Vibia because he was infatuated with a young man named Antinous?

a. Nero

b. Hadrian

c. Otho

d. Claudius

12. Rome is often said to have been the first city in the world to record a population of what?

a. 1,000 people

b. 10,000 people

c. 100,000 people

d. 1,000,000 people

13. The so-called Twelve Tables formed the basis of the Roman what?

a. Legal system

b. Church

c. Economy

d. Military

14. Which of these was NOT a popular dish on Ancient Roman dining tables?

a. Lamb's brains

b. Stuffed dormice

c. Flamingo tongues

d. Cold tomato soup

15. What would a person in Ancient Rome have done with a *cithara*?

    a. Played it
    b. Worn it
    c. Danced it
    d. Rode it

16. Which major European city did the Romans know as Lutetia?

    a. Berlin
    b. Athens
    c. Paris
    d. Copenhagen

17. Emperor Commodus was one of Rome's youngest-serving emperors. How old was he when he took over from his father Marcus Aurelius?

    a. 6
    b. 16
    c. 26
    d. 36

18. The Romans are well known for building straight roads, as direct routes allowed their armies to reach their outposts and battlefields more swiftly than more winding ones. In fact, the Roman road network was so successful that they built more than 50,000 miles of hard-surfaced highway across their empire. True or false?

SOLUTIONS

1. C. Julius Caesar. In fact, Calpurnia was Caesar's third (or, in some accounts, fourth) wife.
2. A. Emperors. No less than four emperors ruled in quick succession in 69 CE – Galba, Otho, Vitellius, and Vespasian.
3. C. July. It's named in honor of Julius Caesar.
4. B. Little boots. A caliga was a Roman military shoe. According to legend, Caligula - whose birthname was Gaius Caesar Augustus Germanicus - is thought to have gained the nickname by which he became known across Europe from his habit as a child of wearing his father's boots.
5. D. Predicted the future. An auspex was essentially a seer or fortune-teller who used the flightpaths of birds as omens to predict the future. The word *auspicious* comes from the same root.
6. False. It's certainly true that many people believe this tale to be true, but the only equivalent procedure to a C-section in the ancient world always ended up killing the mother; and Caesar's mother Aurelia lived for several decades after her son was born. In fact, the word *caesarian* is nothing more than a corruption of *cadere*, the Latin word for "to cut."
7. D. Marry his daughter. Nero only had one child, his daughter Claudia Augusta, but she died of an unknown illness just five months after birth.
8. A. Cicero.
9. A. Poet. Horace was the author of several acclaimed works of Ancient Roman poetry and literature, including his *Satires*, *Odes*, and *Epistles*.
10. B. Tiberius.
11. B. Hadrian. In fact, Emperor Hadrian was so enamored of Antinous that after his young lover died in Egypt in mysterious circumstances in 130 CE, Hadrian had him deified and instigated a religious cult in his honor. For the next 300 years, the emperor's male lover was worshipped by a growing cult of young Romans, until it fell victim of charges of paganism in the 4th century CE.
12. D. 1,000,000 people. Rome is believed to have already grown to one million inhabitants sometime in the 2nd century BCE.
13. A. Legal system. The *Lex Duodecim Tabularum*, or "Laws of the Twelve Tables," were written down in 449 BCE and remained the basis of Roman law for the remainder of the empire.

14. D. Cold tomato soup. They may be a staple of Italian cuisine today, but tomatoes are native to the Americas and were not brought to Europe until the 1500s.
15. A. Played it. It was a kind of U-shaped harp-like lute.
16. C. Paris.
17. B. 16.
18. True. The Roman road system extended from England to the Euphrates River in the Middle East.

DID YOU KNOW?

At its greatest extent, the Roman Empire covered approximately 1.7 million square miles.

4.
MYTHS, LEGENDS, & FOLKLORE

Many of the world's most ancient peoples and cultures - as well as many of those that followed them! They believed in gods, monsters, tales, and supernatural forces far beyond those we hold true today. Covering everything from the gods and goddesses of the Aztecs and Incas to the myths of Greece and Rome and the folklore of medieval Europe, how much of this quiz dedicated to the world's most ancient and longest-established legends can you answer correctly?

1. According to Ancient Greek myth, who killed the hero Achilles?

   a. Paris
   b. Agamemnon
   c. Helen
   d. Hector

2. Which of these peoples believe in a grand ancestral period in the history of the Earth known as the "Dreamtime"?

   a. Indigenous Australians
   b. Nubian Africans
   c. Breton French
   d. Ojibwe Americans

3. Known for his powerful hammer, *Mjölnir*, what was the name of the Norse god of thunder?

4. In the stories of the famous outlaw Robin Hood, Robin is seen as loyal to which displaced English king - and an enemy of his supposed successor, Prince John?

   a. Edward I
   b. Richard I
   c. Stephen
   d. William I

5. In Egyptian mythology, which major goddess was the mother of Ra and considered the principal female deity of the sky?

   a. Hathor
   b. Isis
   c. Maat
   d. Nut

6. In which European culture's mythology is the center of the known world focused on a gigantic yew tree known as *Yggdrasil*?

   a. Norse
   b. Roman
   c. Greek
   d. Minoan

7. True or false: The Incan people worshipped a god named Urcuchillay, whose sole role was to oversee their herds of llamas.

8. According to the famous legend, who was the captain of the ship *Argo*?

   a. Odysseus
   b. Hercules
   c. Achilles
   d. Jason

9. In the mythology of the Seneca people of Lake Ontario, the monster Djieien was portrayed as a gigantic six foot tall...what?

   a. Beaver
   b. Spider
   c. Possum
   d. Mantis

10. The Egyptian goddess Bastet - effigies of whom were often considered talismans, used to protect people from ill fortune - was portrayed with the head of what venerated animal?

    a. Ibis
    b. Jackal
    c. Eagle
    d. Cat

11. In Greek mythology, what kind of creature was Arges, who was said to have fashioned Zeus' thunderbolt during his war with the Titans?

    a. Gorgon
    b. Harpy
    c. Cyclops
    d. Minotaur

12. Tamoanchan is the legendary origin of all the peoples of the world in which ancient civilization's mythology?

    a. Aztec
    b. Babylonian
    c. Carthaginian
    d. Parthian

13. Who was the Roman equivalent of the Greek goddess of the hunt, Artemis?

    a. Diana
    b. Ceres
    c. Juno
    d. Luna

14. In Japanese folklore, a creature known as a *kappa* - a kind of turtle-like monster - has a hole filled with water permanently in its head. But what happens to the kappa if the hole is empty of water?

    a. It becomes invisible
    b. It turns into a human
    c. It loses its powers
    d. It grows wings

15. According to at least one version of the famous Greek myth, the legendary winged horse Pegasus gained life when what equally legendary monster was killed?

    a. Medusa
    b. Kraken
    c. Typhon
    d. Siren

16. In Egyptian folklore, the Sphinx had the body and limbs of which animal?

    a. Lion
    b. Wolf
    c. Scorpion
    d. Snake

17. According to a famous story, Eris, the Greek goddess of discord and disagreement, caused a furor at a wedding ceremony attended by many of the gods and goddesses of Mount Olympus when she threw what onto the banquet table?

    a. A ring
    b. A coin
    c. An apple
    d. A fish

18. Which of these legendary creatures was believed to have a lethal gaze, a single glace of which could kill a person or turn them instantly to stone?

    a. Griffon
    b. Phoenix
    c. Dragon
    d. Basilisk

SOLUTIONS

1. A. Paris. Having abducted Helen of Troy to take as his own wife - sparking the Trojan War - Paris later killed Achilles with an arrow, striking him in the only part of his body that was vulnerable to injury, his foot.
2. A. Indigenous Australians. Although the Dreamtime, or the Dreaming, is a widely used term today, the term is not an original Aboriginal expression. Instead, it was invented by a 19th-century Australian anthropologist and ethnologist named Francis Gillen, who studied and recorded many of the native Australian cultures' traditions.
3. Thor.
4. B. Richard I. Better known as Richard the Lionheart, Richard was absent from England during most of his reign fighting in the Crusades - leaving a longstanding vacuum of royal power his brother, John, was all too keen to fill.
5. A. Hathor.
6. A. Norse.
7. True. Urcuchillay himself was often portrayed as a multicolored llama!
8. D. Jason. Hence Jason's crewmates, on the way to retrieve the Golden Fleece, were known as the Argonauts.
9. B. Spider. According to Seneca tradition, Djieien could not easily be killed because his life force - his heart - was always kept buried below the ground.
10. D. Cat. The Egyptians famously worshiped cats, hence Bastet's association with protection and fortune.
11. C. Cyclops. According to Hesiod's version of the tale, Arges was the leader of three one-eyed brothers - the others were Brontes and Steropes. All three were said to have helped Zeus fashion weaponry for his war with the Titans.
12. A. Aztec. Tamoanchan is the supposed native home of all the Mesoamerican peoples in several local mythologies, most notably the Aztecs.
13. A. Diana. Ceres was the Roman goddess of cultivation (equivalent to Demeter), Juno was a marriage deity (equivalent to Hera), and Luna was the goddess of the Moon (equivalent to Selene).
14. C. It loses its powers.

15. A. Medusa. After Perseus cut off Medusa's head, one version of the myth claims Pegasus flew out of her open neck.
16. A. Lion. It also had a human head and the wings of an eagle.
17. C. An apple. Inscribed on the so-called Apple of Discord (which was made of solid gold) were the words "For the Fairest" - this instantly caused a bitter dispute between the goddesses Hera, Athena, and Aphrodite over who best deserved to keep it.
18. D. Basilisk. A legendary serpent-like creature, variously said to be anywhere from a foot to several yards long, the basilisk takes its name from a Greek word meaning "king," as it was considered by some ancient writers to be the king of reptiles.

DID YOU KNOW?

It's been suggested that Robin Hood's name is a pun - or perhaps even a job description! Some historical accounts suggest his name may have been coined to mean he was a "robber" in the wood.

5.
ANCIENT RULERS

From pharaohs to kings and sultans to emperors, the ancient world was ruled over by a grand array of impressive and imposing leaders. We've already had questions so far here on the likes of Julius Caesar, Philip of Macedon, and King Tutankhamun - but here's a quiz dedicated to rulers of all kinds from across the ancient world…

1. Ruling over Ancient China for more than 700 years, 1046 to 256 BCE, what was the longest-lasting dynasty in Chinese history?

   a. Xin
   b. Zhou
   c. Shang
   d. Xia

2. Which ancient great leader was known for his friendship - and possible relationship - with one of his generals, Hephaestion?

   a. Darius III of Persia
   b. Alexander the Great
   c. Caligula
   d. Genghis Khan

3. The famous temple complex at Abu Simbel in Southern Egypt was the work of which great pharaoh, who commissioned several grand statues of himself to be built around the site?

   a. Amenhotep
   b. Akhenaten
   c. Ptolemy
   d. Ramses II

4. True or false: Shakespeare's play *King Lear* is said to have been based on the life of a genuine king of Ancient Celtic Britain.

5. Which ancient Chinese ruler was the founder of the Qin dynasty, the first Chinese leader to rule over a united China, and the first ruler in the country's history to take the title of emperor?

   a. Mu
   b. Shi Huang
   c. Feizi
   d. Huiwen

6. What ancient English city - a former capital of England - was famously laid to waste by the Celtic warrior queen Boudica in 61 CE?

    a. Colchester
    b. York
    c. Nottingham
    d. Durham

7. The word of an ancient king of Babylonia, what is the Code of Hammurabi?

    a. Atlas
    b. Guide to the zodiac
    c. Set of laws
    d. Mathematical textbook

8. The Roman emperor Trajan was the first emperor in Rome's history not to have been...what?

    a. Black-haired
    b. Born in Italy
    c. Right-handed
    d. Married

9. Having reigned for more than 68 years in the 7th century CE, Pacal the Great is one of the longest-serving rulers in history. But over which ancient region did he rule?

    a. Egypt
    b. Babylonia
    c. India
    d. Mayan Empire

10. Which Egyptian pharaoh of the 18th Dynasty is known for his military prowess and tactical shrewdness, and supposedly never lost a single battle during his reign as king?

    a. Amenhotep III
    b. Ramses II
    c. Khufu
    d. Thutmose III

11. What was the famous Egyptian queen Cleopatra's regnal number?

a. Cleopatra I
b. Cleopatra III
c. Cleopatra V
d. Cleopatra VII

12. Which ancient kingdom had rulers named Cyrus, Cambyses, and Artaxerxes?

a. Bavaria
b. Bohemia
c. Persia
d. Tripoli

13. Said to have been founded by Emperor Jimmu in 660 BCE, which Asian country's monarchy is said to be the oldest continuous hereditary monarchy in the world?

a. Japan
b. Thailand
c. Cambodia
d. Bangladesh

14. Which ancient Athenian statesman and ruler is said to have commissioned the construction of the Parthenon in the 5th century BCE?

a. Solon
b. Pericles
c. Cleon
d. Alcibiades

15. Ruling the early 4th century CE, who was famously the first Roman Emperor to convert to Christianity?

16. Known for his victory over Julius Caesar at the Battle of Gergovia, Vercingetorix was an ancient ruler of which European tribe?

a. Franks
b. Gauls
c. Celts
d. Saxons

17. Atilla the Hun is an infamous 5th- century figure in the history of what continent?

    a. Europe
    b. Africa
    c. Asia
    d. South America

18. Known for uniting much of Western Europe for the first time since the fall of the Roman Empire, which famous ancient ruler was the son of a king and queen named Pepin the Short and Bertrada of Laon?

    a. Ivan the Terrible
    b. Canute
    c. Charles I
    d. Charlemagne

SOLUTIONS

1. B. Zhou. The Zhou dynasty rose to power in China following the defeat of the earlier Shang dynasty at the Battle of Muye in the 11th century BCE.

2. B. Alexander the Great. Having been childhood friends, Alexander and Hephaestion remained close their entire lives (and, according to some accounts, eventually became lovers) until Hephaestion's untimely death at the age of just 32 in 324 BCE. Alexander was said to be distraught with grief, and requested the oracle at Siwa, in northern Egypt, to grant his friend divine status after his death. Alexander himself died just a matter of months later.

3. D. Ramses II. Better known as Ramses the Great, Pharaoh Ramses II is said to have overseen more grand building projects during his reign than any other pharaoh in Egyptian history.

4. True. Known as Leir of Britain, some historians believe the king ruled over Celtic Britain sometime in the 8th century BCE.

5. B. Shi Huang. Also known as Qin Shi Huang, Emperor Shi Huang ruled over China for a relatively brief 11 years in the late 200s BCE - yet adopted a title for himself, Emperor of China, that would be retained by every other Chinese sovereign for the next 2,000 years.

6. A. Colchester.

7. C. Set of laws. Hammurabi was king of Babylon in the mid-1700s BCE, during which time he introduced the renowned set of laws now bearing his name. According to tradition, the king was said to have been told the laws by Shamash, the Babylonian god of justice.

8. B. Born in Italy. Trajan was born in Hispania Baetica - modern-day Spain - in 53 CE.

9. D. Mayan Empire. Pacal ruled for 68 years and 33 days, ranking him alongside the likes of Queen Victoria, Elizabeth II, and Louis XIV as one of history's longest-reigning leaders.

10. D. Thutmose III.

11. D. Cleopatra VII. In full, she was known as Cleopatra VII Thea Philopator - literally, "Seventh Queen Cleopatra, Father-loving Goddess."

12. C. Persia.

13. A. Japan. Although reliable historical records only date back to the 6th century CE, traditionally the Japanese royal family is said to have a lineage stretching back more than 2,600 years.
14. B. Pericles. Although he only ever served as a general (and so was never given any royal or ruling titles in Ancient Athens), Pericles' overseeing of the city was part of its Golden Age. It was during his control that many of the city's major artistic and architectural projects were commissioned, and the city established itself as the de facto center of Ancient Greece.
15. Constantine.
16. B. Gauls.
17. A. Europe. Atilla oversaw a vast empire of eastern European peoples - not just Huns, but Bulgars and Ostrogoths too - for almost 20 years, from 434 CE to his death in 453 CE.
18. D. Charlemagne.

DID YOU KNOW?

At one point, Darius the Great of Persia held at least five different grandiose titles, including King of Babylon, Pharaoh of Egypt, King of Countries, King of Kings - and, of course, King of Persia!

6.
THE VIKINGS

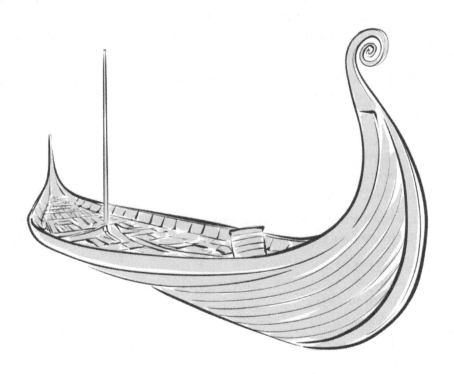

For more than 300 years, from the late 8th to the early 11th centuries, the Vikings - a general term for a maritime people from Scandinavia, in northern Europe - established themselves a reputation as expert seafarers, courageous explorers and adventurers, and bloodthirsty invaders and conquerors. Although it is for their raids on the coasts of Britain, Ireland, and the northern fringes of continental Europe that they are best known for today, in their time the Vikings voyaged as far south as the coasts of Africa, the Middle East, and the Mediterranean, and as far west from Europe as Greenland, Canada, Newfoundland, and the Atlantic coast of the United States. In fact, the Vikings are said to have been the first Europeans in history to have explored North America, with a Viking sailor named Gunnbjörn Ulfsson known to have arrived in Greenland in the 10th century CE! But what do you know about the Vikings?

1. The Vikings explored and invaded so much of the surrounding European continent that some places are named after them - including which famous region of France?

   a. Côte d'Azur
   b. Normandy
   c. Brittany
   d. The Dordogne

2. In what ancient English kingdom is the holy island of Lindisfarne, which was famously attacked and pillaged by the Vikings in 793 CE?

   a. Mercia
   b. Wessex
   c. Northumbria
   d. Kent

3. Which of these days of the week is NOT named after a Norse god or goddess?

   a. Wednesday
   b. Thursday
   c. Friday
   d. Saturday

4. True or false: Despite popular belief, the Vikings are not thought to have worn horned helmets.

5. In Norse mythology, what was unusual about Odin's horse Sleipnir?

    a. It had two heads

    b. It had four wings

    c. It had a snake's tail

    d. It had eight legs

6. In the Viking world, what was the Oseberg?

    a. A ship

    b. A palace

    c. A lighthouse

    d. A prison

7. What language did the Vikings speak?

    a. English

    b. Norse

    c. Celtic

    d. Breton

8. Valhalla was the Vikings' version of…what?

    a. Church

    b. Marriage

    c. Money

    d. The afterlife

9. Believed to have been made in Viking Norway sometime in the 12th century, what was famously discovered on a beach on the island of Lewis in northwest Scotland in 1831?

    a. A golden sword

    b. An ivory chess set

    c. An oak bed

    d. A silver cauldron

10. True or false: To the Vikings themselves, the word *Viking* was considered a job title.

11. The first European settler to ever land and then live in Greenland was a Viking named…what?

    a. Iver the Bad

    b. Erik the Red

c. Thoren the Sad

d. Leif the Glad

12. Viking funerals famously sometimes involved placing the deceased in a longship, casting it out to sea, and setting fire to it. Sometimes, though, the deceased was placed in a ship, and then both they and the ship were...what?

a. Buried underground

b. Placed in a cave

c. Thrown from a cliffside

d. Sunk in a lake

13. Who was the Vikings' god of war?

a. Heimdall

b. Thor

c. Odin

d. Loki

14. What did some Viking men use caustic lye soap to do to their hair?

a. Curl it

b. Bleach it

c. Shave it

d. Gel it

15. Not all the Vikings were plunderers. In fact, in the 10th century, an elite band of Swedish Vikings ended up in Byzantium working as...what?

a. Cooks

b. Bodyguards

c. Gladiators

d. Miners

16. In Viking mythology, one of Thor's mortal enemies was a creature called Jormungand. What was it?

a. A giant wolf

b. A giant whale

c. A giant boar

d. A giant snake

17. Viking society traditionally had three classes or levels: jarls, karls, and...what?

    a. Spalls
    b. Stalls
    c. Thralls
    d. Falls

18. We use it a lot more generally today, but what did the word *thing* mean to the Vikings?

    a. Weapon
    b. Man
    c. Boat
    d. Council

SOLUTIONS

1. B. Normandy. The central portion of France's north coast, Normandy is named after the "North Men" - that is, Vikings - who raided and settled it in a series of attacks beginning in the 700s CE.
2. C. Northumbria.
3. D. Saturday. While Wednesday, Thursday, and Friday are named after the Viking gods Odin (or Woden), Thor, and Frigg, respectively, Saturday is a hangover from the Romans, and is literally "Saturn's Day."
4. True! The image may be an enduring one, but Viking helmets tended to be fairly straightforward headguards. The idea that the Vikings had horns atop their head may have been a rumor instigated by early European Christians, to give the Viking invaders a more devilish reputation.
5. D. It had eight legs.
6. A. A ship. The Oseberg is one of a handful of Viking longships to have survived intact through to the modern day. It is now housed on display in a museum in Oslo.
7. B. Norse. Or, more specifically, Old Norse - the same ancient language from which the modern languages of Norwegian, Swedish, and Danish are now descended.
8. D. The afterlife. Valhalla was one of the 12 realms of Asgard, the dwelling place of the Norse gods.
9. B. An ivory chess set. Now partly housed in London's British Museum, the so-called Lewis Chess Men comprised more than 80 walrus ivory chess pieces.
10. True. *Viking* is not a regional name, nor the name of a tribe, for example, but rather an occupational title, equivalent to something like 'seafarer' or 'buccaneer.'
11. B. Erik the Red. Properly named Erik Thorvaldsson, Erik the Red was one of the most famed explorers and seafarers of 10th-century Nordic Europe.
12. A. Buried underground. Entire longships were buried in gigantic graves for some high-ranking and important Viking and Norse people, several of which have been discovered at sites across northern Europe.
13. C. Odin.

14. B. Bleach it. Red hair was common among the Vikings, but blonde or fair hair was much desired - leading some Viking men to use lye to lighten it!
15. B. Bodyguards. The so-called Varangian Guard, which also included a handful of Anglo-Saxon citizens from England, as well as Vikings from Sweden, were personal bodyguards to the emperors of Byzantium until the 1300s.
16. D. A giant snake. Also known as the World Serpent, Jormungand's body was said to be coiled around the Earth, lying deep beneath the sea.
17. C. Thralls. The jarls were the chiefs, the karls were the workers - chiefly farmers, craftsmen, artisans, and sailors - while the thralls were the serfs or slaves.
18. D. Council. A *thing* was originally a public meeting or assembly, at which various issues could be discussed. Many of the parliaments of the Scandinavian countries -like the Icelandic Althing, or Norwegian Storting - still contain elements of the word in its original sense today!

DID YOU KNOW?

The Vikings apparently had excellent personal hygiene - excavations of their sites have unearthed the likes of razor blades, tweezers, and combs.

7.
THE DARK AGES

The Dark Ages is the name given to the period of European history following the gradual demise (and eventual collapse) of the Roman Empire and ending with the Italian Renaissance.

The precise start and end dates of the Dark Ages are unclear and not widely agreed, however, with some sources claiming the era began as far back as the 5th century CE and lasted the next 1,000 years!

Referring to this grand period of history as the Dark Ages - a reference to the cultural "darkness" that followed the "enlightenment" of Rome - is a controversial issue among historians today, however, as this era was not as uncultured nor as anti-intellectual as it is often presumed.

In fact, this period included the lives of a great many significant historical figures, as well as many hugely important works of art, music, and invention. Time to shine a light on your Dark Ages knowledge!

1. The Hundred Years' War took place during the Dark Ages, between which two European superpowers?

    a. Germany and Poland
    b. Italy and Greece
    c. Spain and Portugal
    d. England and France

2. Also, despite its name, the Hundred Years' War actually lasted for…?

    a. 29 years
    b. 55 years
    c. 98 years
    d. 116 years

3. Which ancient Danish king of England, who ruled in the 11th century, is said to have once sat on a beach in an attempt to command the waves to retreat?

    a. Alfred
    b. Ethelred
    c. Arthur
    d. Canute

4. A significant figure in medieval England, what was the name of the king known as The Confessor?

a. Edward

b. Henry

c. William

d. Stephen

5. As what did the German Abbess Hildegard of Bingen become known in 12th-century Europe?

a. Painter

b. Sculptor

c. Composer

d. Dancer

6. The Norman Conquest of England occurred during the Dark Ages - in what year?

a. 966

b. 1066

c. 1166

d. 1266

7. Which English king was forced by his rebelling barons to sign the Magna Carta document in 1215?

a. Richard I

b. John

c. Charles I

d. Edward III

8. The explorer Marco Polo was born at the height of the Dark Ages in 1254, in which European city?

a. Venice

b. Lisbon

c. Antwerp

d. Vienna

9. Several Eastern European regions - including Bulgaria, Poland, and Hungary were invaded in the mid-13th century by which attacking force?

a. Parthians

b. Egyptians

c. Mongols

d. Vikings

10. The world's oldest continually active university was founded in 1088 in what Italian city?

    a. Rome

    b. Bologna

    c. Palermo

    d. Naples

11. The world's second oldest university and the oldest in the English-speaking world - was founded in England barely a decade later in 1096. Where?

    a. Berwick

    b. Oxford

    c. Edinburgh

    d. York

12. In what European country did The Peasant's Revolt take place in 1381?

    a. France

    b. Sweden

    c. Denmark

    d. England

13. In what European country was the theologian and philosopher Thomas Aquinas born in 1225?

    a. Portugal

    b. Albania

    c. Sweden

    d. Italy

14. In the late 1300s, the so-called Great Schism threatened to break apart the Catholic church when a series of rival popes established their own papal palace outside of Rome, in which French city?

    a. Paris

    b. Avignon

    c. Perpignan

    d. Nice

15. The English king Richard the Lionheart died suddenly and unexpectedly in 1199, when he was struck by a rogue arrow fired idly over a wall while he was besieging a town in which country?

   a. Turkey
   b. Italy
   c. Poland
   d. France

16. Which figure of the later medieval period is credited with inventing the printing press?

   a. William Caxton
   b. William Hogarth
   c. Johannes Gutenberg
   d. Jean Brito

17. In 1422, following the deaths of both the English king Henry V and the French king Charles VII, who became the king of both nations - despite being less than a year old at the time?

   a. Richard III
   b. Edward V
   c. Charles II
   d. Henry VI

18. Established in 1478 by the king and queen of Spain, by what name is the so-called Tribunal of the Holy Office better known?

SOLUTIONS

1. D. England and France. The war was sparked by a series of English monarchs' claims to the throne of France.
2. D. 116 years. The war lasted from 1337–1453.
3. D. Canute.
4. A. Edward. Edward the Confessor was the last king of medieval England's ruling House of Wessex, over which he reigned from 1042 until his death in 1066.
5. C. Composer. Around 70 pieces of music written by Hildegard survive, including her renowned allegorical musical play, *Ordo Virtutum*, written in 1151.
6. B. 1066.
7. B. John.
8. A. Venice. At the time, Venice was its own independent republic, situated high on Europe's Adriatic Sea.
9. C. Mongols. Led by two of the grandsons of Genghis Khan, the Mongols pushed west out of Mongolia in the 13th century, arriving in Europe in the 1220s. They won a series of decisive victories over several European powers, before retreating around two decades later.
10. B. Bologna. Legal teaching is believed to have commenced on the site of the University of Bologna in 1088, but tuition under the church had already been going on in the area for even longer than that.
11. B. Oxford. Some accounts suggest Oxford might be the world's oldest university, but the university's own records claim classes there began in 1096.
12. D. England. Led by an English worker named Wat Tyler, the Peasant's Revolt was a short-lived rebellion against the tax laws of King Richard II.
13. D. Italy. Aquinas - a Dominican friar and priest, as well as a noted philosopher and thinker - took his name from the tiny Sicilian town of Aquino.
14. B. Avignon.
15. D. France. Richard was on his way back to England following the Third Crusade when he was killed besieging the French town of Chalus.

16. C. Johannes Gutenberg. Caxton is credited with bringing the printing press to the English-speaking world in 1476, but it was Gutenberg who invented the movable type printing process.
17. D. Henry VI. In fact, Henry was just nine months old when his father, Henry V, died.
18. The Spanish Inquisition.

DID YOU KNOW?

Richard the Lionheart, King Richard I, became engaged to be married when he was nine years old!

8.
HISTORY OF ASIA

From the rulers of Ancient China to the Mongol invasion of Europe, we've already touched on some of the remarkable history of Asia here, but how much about what else has happened on the world's largest continent do you know? Take a deep dive into the past - covering more than 5,000 years of history - in this mind-bending quiz...

1. The Taj Mahal was built in India by the fifth Mughal emperor, Shah Jahan, in 1631. What did he intend it to be?

   a. Temple
   b. Tomb
   c. Market
   d. Museum

2. Which ancient people are credited with producing the first wheel-turned pots more than 5,000 years ago?

   a. Sumerians
   b. Parthians
   c. Mongols
   d. Chinese

3. The legendary Emperor Ashoka, whose empire ruled over much of central Asia in the 3rd century BCE, was from which modern-day country?

   a. Singapore
   b. Russia
   c. Mongolia
   d. India

4. What Asian capital city is believed to have been inhabited as far back as 6000 BCE, making it the oldest capital in the world?

   a. Tokyo
   b. Beijing
   c. Damascus
   d. Bangkok

5. Where was the prophet Muhammad born in the 6th century CE?

   a. Riyadh
   b. Tel Aviv

c. Jerusalem

d. Mecca

6. Which great Asian nation and empire are credited with the invention of early forms of glass, paper, gunpowder, porcelain clay, and the compass?

   a. India

   b. Afghanistan

   c. China

   d. Iran

7. In what century did the First Crusade to the Holy Land take place?

   a. 8th

   b. 9th

   c. 10th

   d. 11th

8. True or false: It is impossible to investigate the tomb of the first emperor of the Qin dynasty, Qin Shi Huang, because his body is surrounded by poisonous metal.

9. Temüjin was the birth name of what famous figure from Asian history?

   a. Confucius

   b. Genghis Khan

   c. Buddha

   d. Darius the Great

10. The ancient kingdom of Parthia, which flourished for more than four centuries, was centered around what modern-day Asian country?

   a. Bangladesh

   b. Myanmar

   c. Iran

   d. Yemen

11. Personally bestowed by the emperor, what title was held by the highest-ranking military leaders and rulers of ancient Japan?

12. Saadi Shirazi - better known as Sadi - was a famous Persian… what?

   a. Poet

b. Sculptor

c. Lawmaker

d. Mathematician

13. By what two-word name is the trade route officially designated as the Network of Chang'an-Tianshan - now a World Heritage Site - better known?

14. What major world religion was founded in the Punjab region of India sometime around the end of the 15th century?

a. Islam

b. Buddhism

c. Sikhism

d. Shintoism

15. In the 7th century CE, the capital of the Muslim world was temporarily shifted from the holy city of Medina to what Middle Eastern capital?

a. Amman

b. Aden

c. Damascus

d. Doha

16. True or false: As well as being the first country in the world to have one billion people, in the 12th century, China also became the first country in the world to have more than 100 million inhabitants.

17. The ancient region of Mesopotamia was traditionally said to be bounded by two great...what?

a. Rivers

b. Mountain ranges

c. Lakes

d. Seas

18. In what major Chinese city - a former capital - was the famous Terracotta Army produced for Emperor Qin Shi Huang in the 3rd century BCE?

a. Beijing

b. Nanjing

c. Shanghai

d. Xi'an

SOLUTIONS

1. B. Tomb. The Mughal Emperor intended the Taj Mahal to be a grand tomb or mausoleum, in which to house the body of his favorite wife, Mumtaz Mahal.
2. A. Sumerians. An early foot-powered potter's wheel, known as a tournette or tourney, was in use in the Near East from at least 3400 BCE.
3. D. India. Ashoka ruled over the so-called Magadha Empire from 268–232 BCE.
4. C. Damascus. The capital of Syria. Recent archaeological expeditions and carbon dating experiments have led to suggestions the city may have been inhabited even earlier— - perhaps for more than 10,000 years.
5. D. Mecca.
6. C. China. Having invented an early form of paper, China also became the first nation to introduce banknotes.
7. D. 11th. Led by a coalition of French, Flemish, Spanish, and Italian forces, the First Crusade to reclaim the Holy Land from Muslim rule began in 1096. After a successful campaign, the Crusaders returned to Europe three years later.
8. True! The 3rd century BCE Emperor Qin Shi Huang's gigantic tomb complex covers more than 30 square miles. Archaeologists worry that the tomb of China's first emperor contains deadly booby traps. An ancient Chinese historian wrote that the tomb was filled with mercury and crossbows ready to fire.
9. B. Genghis Khan. Khan's Mongol empire eventually became the largest the world has ever seen.
10. C. Iran. At its height, the Parthian Empire stretched from what is now western Turkey, across Iran, the Caspian Sea, and the northern Middle East, into Pakistan and northern India.
11. Shogun.
12. A. Poet. Completed in 1257, Saadi's anthology of poems Bustan ("The Orchard") is widely considered one of the greatest works of poetry in Asian literature.
13. The Silk Road.

14. C. Sikhism. Now the fifth-most followed religious doctrine in the world, Sikhism is one of the most recently founded of all major world religions.
15. C. Damascus. The city remained the Muslim capital for the next century or so, until it was again relocated, this time to Baghdad.
16. False. China did have a population of 100 million by the late 1100s, but India had reached that milestone earlier - thought to be sometime around 660 CE!
17. A. Rivers. The Tigris and the Euphrates.
18. D. Xi'an.

DID YOU KNOW?

It is thought more than 1,000 elephants were utilized in the construction of the Taj Mahal.

9.
THE 1500S

The 16th century saw the end of the Dark Ages, the beginning of the Renaissance and the Enlightenment, and - in the eyes of many historians - the rise of what would go on to be known as the Western world. This was the era in which Shakespeare, Descartes, Galileo, Nostradamus, and Caravaggio were all born and flourished, each making enormous advances in the arts, sciences, and our understanding of the world around us. So, let's test your knowledge of this most important of eras with this chapter all about the people and events of the 1500s.

1. The future Queen Elizabeth I, Elizabeth Tudor, was born in Greenwich, England, in 1533. Who was her father?

    a. Henry VII
    b. Henry VIII
    c. James I
    d. Charles I

2. The astronomer and scientist Galileo Galilei eventually fell afoul of the Catholic Inquisition and was forced to recant his steadfast belief that...what?

    a. Humans evolved from lesser animals
    b. The Earth was not created in seven days
    c. The story of Noah's Ark was fiction
    d. The Sun was the center of the solar system

3. Which famous explorer and seafarer, who was eventually the subject of a mutiny on his ship *Discovery* and cast adrift in North American waters, was born in England sometime around 1565?

    a. Henry Hudson
    b. Walter Raleigh
    c. James Cook
    d. John Smith

4. The first Russian monarch to be crowned as Tsar of all Russia was born in Moscow in 1530 and reigned as Tsar from 1547 until his death in 1584. Who was he?

    a. Peter the Great
    b. Vasily I
    c. Nicholas I
    d. Ivan the Terrible

5. Born in Paris in 1585, the infamous French clergyman Cardinal Richelieu had a nickname in his time that translates into English as...what?

   a. The Red Eminence
   b. The Blue Distinction
   c. The Gold Importance
   d. The White Fame

6. The tragic Tudor Queen Mary, Queen of Scots, became queen on the death of her father, James V of Scotland - when she was how old?

   a. 6 days
   b. 6 months
   c. 6 years
   d. 66 years

7. As what did Danish polymath Tycho Brahe achieve fame during the 16th century Renaissance?

   a. Composer
   b. Painter
   c. Astronomer
   d. Chemist

8. A member of the famous Medici family of Italy, from 1547 to 1559 Catherine de' Medici was queen of which European superpower?

   a. England
   b. France
   c. Austria
   d. Spain

9. The Welsh mathematician Robert Recorde is credited with being the first arithmetician to use what symbol in his 1557 textbook, *The Whetstone of Witte*?

   a. Zero, 0
   b. Equals sign, =
   c. Decimal point, .
   d. Dollar sign, $

10. In what city was the artist Caravaggio born in 1571?

a. Milan

b. Sarajevo

c. Athens

d. Vienna

11. True or false: Despite his son going on to become the world's most celebrated playwright, William Shakespeare's father was illiterate.

12. Henry VIII married his sixth and final wife in 1543, just four years before his death. What was her name?

a. Jane Seymour

b. Anne of Cleves

c. Catherine Parr

d. Catherine Howard

13. Born in 1503, what nationality was the renowned seer and astrologer Nostradamus?

a. French

b. Chinese

c. Greek

d. Egyptian

14. The longest reigning sultan of the Ottoman Empire, Suleiman I, rose to power in 1520 and ruled until his death in 1566. By what nickname was he known?

a. Suleiman the Intelligent

b. Suleiman the Proficient

c. Suleiman the Patient

d. Suleiman the Magnificent

15. In 1517, the German theologian Martin Luther famously nailed his Ninety-Five Theses to the door of a church in which German town?

a. Wittenberg

b. Magdeburg

c. Leipzig

d. Dresden

16. The famous Italian statesman and author Machiavelli died in Florence in 1527. What was the title of his famous political treatise, which was published after his death in 1532?

a. *The King*
b. *The Queen*
c. *The Prince*
d. *The Princess*

17. True or false: The English explorer Francis Drake circumnavigated the globe in the late 1500s. The trip took him 24 years to complete.

18. The religious leader and scholar John Calvin - the founder of Protestant Calvinism - was born in 1509 and died in 1564. Despite his English-sounding name, what nationality was he?

    a. Dutch
    b. French
    c. Polish
    d. Portuguese

SOLUTIONS

1. B. Henry VIII. Elizabeth was the daughter of the Tudor King Henry and his second wife, Anne Boleyn.
2. D. The Sun was the center of the solar system. Galileo's championing of the theory of heliocentrism - that the Earth orbits around the Sun - was considered heresy by Pope Urban VIII. Eventually tried by the Inquisition in the early 1600s, he spent the remainder of his life under house arrest.
3. A. Henry Hudson. The namesake of North America's Hudson Bay, Hudson's fate after he was cast adrift by his crew in 1611 remains unknown.
4. D. Ivan the Terrible.
5. A. The Red Eminence. Cardinal Richelieu was the very first *l'Eminence Rouge* - a nickname referring both to the traditional red robes of a Catholic cardinal, and the traditional title, Grand Eminence, by which they are addressed.
6. A. 6 days. Mary was the only surviving legitimate child of James V of Scotland, and hence his immediate heir to the throne despite her young age.
7. C. Astronomer. Brahe - known for the discovery of supernovae, among countless other astronomical observations - was the last great astronomer before the invention of the telescope in the early 1600s.
8. B. France. Catherine was the wife of the French king Henry II, and the mother of a further three French monarchs - Francis II, Charles IX, and Henry III.
9. B. Equals sign, =. The symbol was originally much longer than it tends to be written today, with Recorde explaining his choice of the symbol's appearance by stating that "no two things can be more equal" than a pair of parallel lines.
10. A. Milan.
11. True. As was common for tradesmen and businessmen without formal education at the time, John Shakespeare could not read or write; when required to sign official documents, he would draw a picture of a pair of glovers' compasses instead.
12. C. Catherine Parr. Catherine went on to outlived Henry by almost two years.

13. A. French. Nostradamus was born Michel de Nostredame in Provence.
14. D. Suleiman the Magnificent.
15. A. Wittenberg. At the time, Luther was a professor at the University of Wittenberg in Saxony.
16. C. *The Prince*.
17. False. Drake's circumnavigation was actually remarkably swift and took just over three years to complete.
18. B. French. Calvin was born in Noyon, a village in the Picardy region of northern France.

DID YOU KNOW?

She may have been known as the Virgin Queen and remained unmarried her whole life, but Elizabeth I had several romantic suitors - including King Philip II of Spain.

10.
THE AGE OF EXPLORATION

The Age of Exploration is the name given to a lengthy period of history - roughly lasting from the 15th to the 17th century - during which time explorers and seafarers, mainly from Europe, set out across the globe to establish new colonies and trade opportunities. Though perilous and by no means always successful, many of these explorers' astonishing endeavors proved enormously lucrative for their home nations, and set up important trade routes, markets, and global business opportunities that would endure for centuries to come. Let's test your knowledge of this extraordinary era with this quiz dedicated to some of the world's most famous explorers.

1. With how many ships did Christopher Columbus set sail for the New World in 1492?

    a. 2
    b. 3
    c. 4
    d. 5

2. Which group of nine volcanic islands in the North Atlantic Ocean were discovered by a little-known Portuguese explorer named Diogo de Silves in 1427?

    a. The Falklands
    b. The Shetlands
    c. The Azores
    d. Faroe Islands

3. In 1488, the Portuguese explorer Bartolomeu Dias rounded what he called The Cape of Storms - now the Cape of Good Hope - at the southernmost tip of which landmass?

    a. South America
    b. Africa
    c. India
    d. Greenland

4. Which English king commissioned John Cabot's explorations of North America, during which he discovered Newfoundland in 1497?

    a. Edward II
    b. Richard III
    c. Henry VII

d. Elizabeth I

5. In March 1500, a Spanish explorer and conquistador named Vicente Pinzón became the first European to sight and sail into which famous body of water?

    a. Hudson Bay
    b. The Nile
    c. The Red Sea
    d. The Amazon

6. Portuguese explorer Diogo Dias was the first European to sight which Indian Ocean island in 1500?

    a. Madagascar
    b. Mauritius
    c. Réunion
    d. Java

7. True or false: The island of Bermuda was named after its discoverer.

8. By what name was the Indonesian archipelago of *Maluku*, or the Moluccas, known during the Age of Exploration?

    a. Nice Islands
    b. Choice Islands
    c. Spice Islands
    d. Mice Islands

9. In 1516, Portuguese explorers and traders arrived in a land they named Cochinchina. Where were they?

    a. Vietnam
    b. Somalia
    c. Ghana
    d. Qatar

10. Having traveled around Mexico, which infamous Spanish explorer arrived in the Aztec capital of Tenochtitlan in 1519?

    a. Hernán Cortés
    b. Francisco Pizarro
    c. Alonso de Ojeda
    d. Pedro Arias Dávila

11. What area of Canada was explored by Frenchman Jacques Cartier in 1534?

    a. Yukon
    b. Baffin Island
    c. Vancouver Island
    d. Prince Edward Island

12. In the early 1540s, Spanish explorer Hernando de Soto became the first European to cross which major North American landmark?

    a. The Rocky Mountains
    b. The Mississippi River
    c. The Sonoran Desert
    d. Death Valley

13. What was the name of the ship on which the English explorer Francis Drake completed his circumnavigation of the globe?

    a. Discovery
    b. Endurance
    c. Golden Hind
    d. Investigator

14. While searching for the famous Northwest Passage in the late 16th century, the English explorer and cartographer John Davis discovered the Davis Strait. Between which two regions does it lie?

    a. Norway and Sweden
    b. Greenland and Canada
    c. Cuba and Florida
    d. Russia and Finland

15. Which explorer sailed into what is now Albany, New York, in 1609?

    a. Francis Drake
    b. James Cook
    c. Thomas Button
    d. Henry Hudson

16. True or false: The first Europeans to cross the Himalayas and enter the ancient kingdom of Bhutan were two gold prospectors.

17. French tradesman Jean Nicolet was the first European to discover what major body of water in the early 1630s?

    a. Lake Victoria
    b. Coral Sea
    c. Black Sea
    d. Lake Michigan

18. In 1732, Russian explorer Mikhail Gvozdev was the first Russian to arrive in a region he called "Large Country." How is it known today?

    a. Alaska
    b. Antarctica
    c. Sri Lanka
    d. New Zealand

SOLUTIONS

1. B. 3. The *Niña*, the *Pinta*, and the *Santa Maria*.
2. C. The Azores. Located around 900 miles off the coast of Portugal, the Azores have remained a Portuguese territory ever since.
3. B. Africa.
4. C. Henry VII. Cabot's exploration at the behest of Henry VII - the father of Henry VIII - is believed to be the first European exploration of the coast of North America since the Vikings arrived there almost 500 years earlier.
5. D. The Amazon. Pinzón - who had served as the captain of Columbus' Pinta the previous decade - sailed around 50 miles into the mouth of the Amazon, becoming the first Western explorer to both see and enter the river.
6. A. Madagascar
7. True. His name was Juan de Bermúdez.
8. C. Spice Islands. After the islands' discovery in 1511, Maluku became known in the West for its rich supply of spices including nutmeg and cloves.
9. A. Vietnam.
10. A. Hernán Cortés. Cortés later overthrew the Aztec Empire, before returning to Spain after two decades in Latin America, in 1541.
11. D. Prince Edward Island. Originally subsumed into the French-Canadian colony of Acadia, Prince Edward Island was later claimed by the British and renamed in honor of Edward, the Duke of Kent, the fourth son of King George III.
12. B. The Mississippi River. De Soto later died of a fever on the banks of the Mississippi, thought to be somewhere near what is now the Arkansas–Louisiana border.
13. C. Golden Hind.
14. B. Greenland and Canada. Lying off the east coast of Canada's Baffin Island, the Davis Strait connects the Arctic Ocean to the Labrador Sea.
15. D. Henry Hudson. The river down which Hudson sailed into northern New York now bears his name.
16. False. In fact, they were Portuguese Jesuit missionaries — Estêvão Cacella and João Cabral. Cabral later went on to be the first European to reach Nepal too.

17. D. Lake Michigan. Nicolet is now thought to have been the first European to reach what is now Wisconsin.
18. A. Alaska. Russia remained in control of Alaska from shortly after its discovery until the Alaska Purchase of 1867.

DID YOU KNOW?

Contrary to popular belief, Columbus did not set off on his voyage to prove the Earth was round. In fact, many people even by Columbus' day had already worked that out!

11.
NATIVE AMERICAN HISTORY

To say that different regions of the world were "discovered" during the Age of Exploration is misleading, of course, because a great many of these so-called discoveries were already well known to the native peoples who called them home. This is certainly true of North America, which for centuries was a patchwork of neighboring and interconnecting native nations until European expansion and colonization slowly encroached on the continent and changed it forever.

1. In 1513, Spanish explorer Juan Ponce de Leon landed on continental North America and became the first recorded European to contact Native Americans. In what modern-day state did their meeting take place?

    a. Virginia
    b. Florida
    c. New York
    d. Texas

2. In what year is Pocahontas believed to have been born?

    a. 1510
    b. 1545
    c. 1596
    d. 1635

3. The Trail of Tears is the name given to the forcible removable of more than 60,000 Native American people from their homeland in the mid-1800s. How many tribes were affected by it?

    a. 1
    b. 2
    c. 5
    d. 10

4. The Ancestral Puebloans, also known as the Anasazi people, were a group of Native Americans known for living in houses built…where?

    a. By rivers
    b. In cliffs
    c. In trees
    d. In the Arctic

5. Led by their chief, Opechancanough, which Native American people led the so-called Indian Massacre of 1622 against the colony of Jamestown?

   a. Cherokee
   b. Powhatan
   c. Cree
   d. Athabascan

6. What was the name of the New England Native American tribe who endured a brief war against an alliance of European colonists in the late 1630s, which eventually led to their extinction in the area?

   a. Pequot
   b. Quinnipiac
   c. Abenaki
   d. Menominee

7. Under which British king was the so-called Proclamation of 1763 drawn up, which recognized Native American land claims for the first time and forbade any white settlement west of a line down the Appalachian Mountains?

   a. Charles II
   b. William III
   c. George III
   d. James I

8. In 1769, Franciscan Father Junipero Serra established a Spanish missionary station outside which modern-day city, which later became the scene of fierce fighting and rebellion with the local Native Americans?

   a. Salt Lake City
   b. Houston
   c. San Diego
   d. Washington

9. Which Lakota leader famously led his people against the United States Army in a series of conflicts along the Powder River in Wyoming and Montana in the 1860s?

a. Iron Shell
b. Red Cloud
c. Sitting Bull
d. He Dog

10. True or false: Sacagawea had two young children with her when she accompanied Lewis and Clark on their expedition in the early 1800s.

11. Known for his attempts to unite the native tribes against European colonizers in the early 19th century, what nationality was Tecumseh?

a. Huron
b. Miami
c. Lenape
d. Shawnee

12. Thought to date back more than 1,000 years, what name is given to the longstanding alliance between the Ojibwe, Odawa, and Potawatomi North American Native tribes?

a. The Council of the Three Fires
b. The Council of the Three Birds
c. The Council of the Three Trees
d. The Council of the Three Lakes

13. Which great Apache leader and medicine man was known by a name thought literally to mean "he who yawns"?

a. Geronimo
b. Monoquet
c. Chipeta
d. Barboncito

14. Born sometime around the turn of the 18th to 19th century, Haboguwiga - better known as Glory of the Morning - was the only known female chief of which Wisconsin Native American people?

a. Oneida
b. Sokaogon
c. Fond du Lac
d. Ho-Chunk

15. Which Native American people's traditional origin story claims their ancestors climbed up through underground chambers, or *kivas*, before reaching what they now know as the Fourth World?

    a. Mohave
    b. Navajo
    c. Hopi
    d. Quechan

16. What was the occupation of Sacagawea's French-Canadian husband, Toussaint Charbonneau?

    a. Shipbuilder
    b. Gold miner
    c. Musician
    d. Fur trapper

17. Constructed in rural Mississippi more than 1,500 years ago, Nanih Waiya is a sacred mound in the culture of which native people?

    a. Kickapoo
    b. Osage
    c. Kaw
    d. Choctaw

18. True or false: It has been estimated the indigenous population of North America prior to the arrival of Christopher Columbus was 700,000.

SOLUTIONS

1. B. Florida. Ponce de Leon was later killed while on a second journey to Florida in 1521.
2. C. 1596. Pocahontas was the daughter of Wahunsenacawh, or Chief Powhatan of the Powhatan people.
3. C. 5. The Trail of Tears affected the so-called Five Civilized Tribes — namely the Cherokee, Muscogee, Seminole, Chickasaw, and Choctaw nations.
4. B. In cliffs. The Ancestral Puebloans' so-called Cliff Palace is the largest cliff dwelling in North America.
5. B. Powhatan. The event led to the so-called Anglo-Powhatan Wars, which rumbled on in the Colony of Virginia for almost 40 years.
6. A. Pequot. Around 700 Pequot people were either killed or imprisoned because of the Pequot War, while most of the remaining survivors of the massacre assimilated into other local peoples.
7. C. George III. The Proclamation remains of legal importance to this day, especially in Canada where parts of it remain enshrined in the constitution.
8. C. San Diego.
9. B. Red Cloud. Red Cloud's War - also known as the Bozeman War - lasted from 1866 to 1868.
10. False. She was actually believed to have been around six months pregnant when the expedition set off and had her child in February 1805.
11. D. Shawnee. Tecumseh was later killed in fighting during the War of 1812.
12. A. The Council of the Three Fires. Traditionally, the alliance is said to have been established in 796 CE.
13. A. Geronimo.
14. D. Ho-Chunk.
15. C. Hopi.
16. D. Fur trapper.
17. D. Choctaw.
18. False: Although estimates vary wildly, a typical estimation of the native population in 1492 is seven million, not 700,000.

DID YOU KNOW?

Pocahontas was not Pocahontas' real name, but a childhood nickname thought to mean "little mischievous one."

12.
THE TUDORS

The House of Tudor - led by five monarchs, Henry VII, Henry VIII, Edward VI, Mary I, and Elizabeth I - ruled over England for more than a century, from 1485 to 1603. Their dynasty oversaw some extraordinary cultural and political upheavals both at home in England and around the rest of the world, as Tudor (and in particular, Elizabethan) explorers expanded England's influence around the globe, while the kings' and queens' armies battled wars and invasions back home in Europe. Let's test how much you know about this remarkable era — and its equally remarkable leaders and characters.

1. Despite ruling over England, the origins of the House of Tudor actually lie in...?

    a. Ireland
    b. Wales
    c. France
    d. Scotland

2. The last king of the Plantagenet dynasty, who was Henry VII's predecessor as King of England?

    a. Edward IV
    b. Richard III
    c. Richard III
    d. Henry VI

3. What was the name of Henry VII's wife and future queen, whose younger brothers - the so-called Princes in the Tower - disappeared under mysterious circumstances in the Tower of London in the 1480s?

    a. Elizabeth
    b. Mary
    c. Helen
    d. Eleanor

4. True or False: Henry VIII was five feet four inches tall.

5. It has been estimated that during his reign, Henry VIII ordered how many executions?

    a. 70
    b. 700
    c. 7,000

d. 70,000

6. Henry VIII's first wife, Catherine of Aragon, was already known to him before they wed. How?

   a. She was his sister's friend
   b. She was his mother's maid
   c. She was his daughter's nurse
   d. She was his brother's widow

7. According to some historians, Henry VIII's famously large waistline is thought to have been the indirect result of...what?

   a. A hormonal imbalance
   b. A jousting accident
   c. Misguided dietary advice
   d. His best friend training as a cook

8. Henry VIII was the first English king who demanded to be called "Your Majesty." How did people usually address the king before then?

   a. "Your Grace"
   b. "Your Eminence"
   c. "My Lord"
   d. "Your Honor"

9. How many of Henry VIII's wives were beheaded?

   a. 0
   b. 1
   c. 2
   d. 3

10. With which 16th-century pope did Henry VIII have his longstanding disagreement over the annulment of his marriage to Catherine of Aragon, eventually leading to the formation of the Church of England?

    a. Clement VII
    b. Innocent IV
    c. Pius III
    d. Gregory XII

11. Henry VIII's only son, Edward VI, died young in 1553. How old was he?

a. 15
b. 20
c. 22
d. 27

12. In 1558, England's last territory in France was lost. Where was it?

    a. Calais
    b. Marseille
    c. Avignon
    d. Honfleur

13. What was the name of England's Nine-Day Queen, who briefly claimed the throne on Edward VI's death in 1553, and was later executed the following year?

    a. Matilda
    b. Stephanie
    c. Jane
    d. Emma

14. By marriage, Mary Tudor - later Queen Mary I of England - was also for a time in the mid-16th century the queen of what other European country?

    a. Hungary
    b. Sweden
    c. Spain
    d. Greece

15. Which of these did Mary I once do to her sister, later Queen Elizabeth I?

    a. Attempt to poison her
    b. Set fire to her bedchamber
    c. Throw her in jail
    d. Knock her from her horse

16. Having circumnavigated the world, when he arrived back in England in 1580, Francis Drake was knighted by Elizabeth I in Buckingham Palace. True or false?

17. England under Elizabeth I famously saw an attempted invasion by a fleet of ships sent from which other European superpower in 1588?

a. Italy
b. Germany
c. Norway
d. Spain

18. After the death of Elizabeth I in 1603, the Tudor period came to an end - leading which new royal dynasty to take control of the English throne?

a. Hanover
b. Windsor
c. Stuart
d. Lancaster

SOLUTIONS

1. B. Wales. The first Tudor king, Henry VII, was actually born in Pembrokeshire, on the southwest coast of Wales, in 1457.
2. C. Richard III. It was Richard's defeat at the famous Battle of Bosworth Field in August 1485, that paved the way for Henry Tudor to take to the English throne in his place.
3. A. Elizabeth. In full, Henry's queen was known as Elizabeth of York, and her marriage to Henry marked the end of England's bitter and long-lasting Wars of the Roses.
4. False. Actually, Henry was known to be handsome in his youth, and remarkably tall for the time: he stood at least six feet in height.
5. D. 70,000. Although this figure is an estimate, it is thought Henry oversaw the deaths of approximately 72,000 of his opponents and fiercest critics.
6. D. She was his brother's widow. As husband to Henry's brother Arthur, Catherine briefly held the title of Princess of Wales before his untimely death in 1502.
7. B. A jousting accident. Henry was injured in a fall from his horse during a tournament in 1536, which left him less able to exercise as he grew older.
8. A. "Your Grace." "Grace" or "Highness" (which remains in use in some contexts today) were the usual forms of address for an English monarch until Henry VIII heard the Holy Roman Emperor Charles V being called "Your Majesty" in 1519, and decided he preferred the sound of that instead!
9. C. 2. Anne Boleyn and Catherine Howard.
10. A. Clement VII.
11. A. 15.
12. A. Calais. The port of Calais had been an English possession for more than two centuries, since 1347.
13. C. Jane. Lady Jane Grey - also known as Jane Dudley - was a great-granddaughter of King Henry VII via his daughter, Mary, and therefore first cousin once removed to King Edward VI, her successor Queen Mary I, and Queen Elizabeth I.
14. C. Spain. Mary was the husband and queen of King Philip II of Spain, from January 1556 until her death in 1558.

15. C. Throw her in jail. As a Catholic, Mary faced near continual rebellion from England's protestants during her reign and at one time accused Elizabeth of being involved in a plot to dethrone her and claim England for herself. As a result, Mary had Elizabeth imprisoned for two months until she was convinced of her innocence. Even then, Elizabeth essentially remained under house arrest until 1555.
16. False. Drake was actually knighted on the deck of his ship, the *Golden Hind*, while it was moored in Deptford, on the south bank of the River Thames. As for Buckingham Palace, it wasn't built until 1705!
17. D. Spain. The so-called Spanish Armada was swiftly defeated, and Elizabeth remained in power for another 15 years.
18. C. Stuart. The throne passed to the Scottish king James VI, who became James I of England.

DID YOU KNOW?

When Henry VIII died, his waistline was 54 inches!

13.
THE 1600S

The 17th century saw many of the world's leading nations and civilizations establish themselves even further as global powers - leading to the so-called Spanish Golden Age, and a prolonged period of French progress known as the Grand Siècle. Colonies began to emerge in America, and through international corporations like the Dutch East India Company, lucrative trade routes opened around the world, causing the global economy to flourish.

Elsewhere, the Baroque movement emerged, leading to the production of countless exquisite works of art and music, while the Scientific Revolution saw our understanding of the world reach new and exciting heights. Test how much you know about this extraordinary period of development and progress with these fiendish questions…

1. Often said to be the world's first modern novel, *Don Quixote* was published in two parts in the 17th century, the first in 1605 and the second in 1615. In what language was it written?

    a. Latin
    b. French
    c. Spanish
    d. Italian

2. Originally named "James Fort," in what year was Jamestown - the first permanent English settlement in the Americas - founded?

    a. 1607
    b. 1617
    c. 1627
    d. 1637

3. Which renowned astronomer published his *Laws of Planetary Motion* in 1609, explaining in detail for the first time the orbits of the planets around the sun?

    a. Nicolaus Copernicus
    b. Johannes Kepler
    c. Sir Isaac Newton
    d. Sir Edmund Halley

4. Europe's so-called Thirty Years' War commenced in 1618. Despite its name, it did NOT last 30 years. True or false?

5. The Pilgrims' *Mayflower* arrived in Massachusetts in 1620, where they would later establish their Plymouth Colony. But in what month of that year did they drop anchor in America?

   a. January
   b. April
   c. August
   d. November

6. A European merchant named Peter Minuit is generally credited with securing the purchase of Manhattan Island from the local Lenape people in 1626, exchanging the land for what was recorded at the time as "60 [Dutch] guilders" of saleable goods. In modern terms, how did that equate to at the time?

   a. $24
   b. $24,000
   c. $24,000,000
   d. $2.4 billion

7. Construction on the Taj Mahal began in 1631, in which Indian city?

   a. Goa
   b. Calcutta
   c. Jaipur
   d. Agra

8. Which English king was defeated in the English Civil War of the 1640s, eventually becoming the only king in British history to be beheaded in 1649?

   a. James II
   b. Charles I
   c. William III
   d. George IV

9. After almost three centuries in power, which grand Chinese dynasty fell in 1644, and was replaced by the short-lived Shun dynasty?

   a. Yuan
   b. Ming
   c. Song
   d. Han

10. Which great European philosopher and scientist published his groundbreaking *Principles of Philosophy* in 1644?

    a. Descartes
    b. Locke
    c. Leibniz
    d. Montesquieu

11. What was the name of the English Puritan ruler Oliver Cromwell's son, who took over his reign as Lord Protector on his father's death in 1658?

    a. John
    b. Richard
    c. Christian
    d. Arnold

12. Which French king oversaw the construction of the famed Palace of Versailles, which began in 1661?

    a. Henry IV
    b. Louis XIV
    c. Louis XVI
    d. Charles III

13. In 1664, the English took control of New York from the Dutch. Under Dutch rule, what had the city been known as?

    a. New Leiden
    b. New Rotterdam
    c. New Hague
    d. New Amsterdam

14. In 1675, a new Royal Observatory was commissioned to be built in what famous area of London?

    a. Hammersmith
    b. Bloomsbury
    c. Greenwich
    d. Mayfair

15. Which great superpower entered into a bitter war with the Ottoman Empire in 1676?

    a. Russia

b. China

c. Egypt

d. India

16. Forces from which modern-day country invaded England in 1688, commencing a year-long period of upheaval known as the Glorious Revolution?

a. Norway

b. Denmark

c. Portugal

d. The Netherlands

17. In what year of the 17th century did the Salem Witch Trials commence in Massachusetts?

a. 1678

b. 1683

c. 1692

d. 1699

18. In what country did the War of the Two Kings break out in 1689, and continue for the next two and a half years?

a. Ireland

b. Italy

c. Indonesia

d. India

SOLUTIONS

1. C. Spanish. Written by Miguel de Cervantes.
2. A. 1607. The colonists set sail from England the previous year and stopped in the Canary Islands and Puerto Rico before landing in America and establishing a new permanent base there in early May.
3. B. Johannes Kepler.
4. False. It lasted from 1618 to 1648.
5. D. November. The Pilgrims had hoped to take two ships to the New World, but delays and problems in chartering both vessels led to them only securing one, which set off from England later than expected. As a result, the Pilgrims had to endure the harsh New England winter almost as soon as they arrived in America.
6. A. $24. The equivalent price in the 2020s has been estimated at just over $1,000.
7. D. Agra. It would take more than 20 years to complete the work.
8. B. Charles I. Fought between the Royalist ("Cavalier") forces, loyal to King Charles, and the republican Parliamentarians (or "Roundheads"), the English Civil War consisted of a series of bloody clashes across England from 1642 to 1651. An early Royalist defeat in 1646 emboldened the Parliamentarian forces under Oliver Cromwell to push for even greater concessions, eventually leading to the English monarchy being abandoned altogether and replaced with a short-lived parliamentary system known as The Protectorate.
9. B. Ming. The Ming dynasty had originally risen to power in 1368.
10. A. Descartes. Written originally in Latin, René Descartes' *Principles of Philosophy* was so groundbreaking in its day that some of the ideas he included in it formed the basis of Sir Isaac Newton's First Law of Motion.
11. B. Richard. Cromwell's Protectorate parliament - which briefly replaced the English monarchy, following his victory in the English Civil War - did not last long under Richard's rule and collapsed the following year. The monarchy was later restored in 1660, with the English King Charles II recalled from exile in France to take his rightful place on the throne once more.
12. B. Louis XIV. Originally the site of little more than a royal hunting lodge and chateau built by Louis XIII, work on Louis XIV's Palace of Versailles would be conducted in stages for the next 50 years. King

Louis moved his government to Versailles in 1682 and remained there until his death. Happily, he lived to see the work at his favorite residence completed, as he died in 1715 - the same year construction of the palace ended.

13. D. New Amsterdam.
14. C. Greenwich. Commissioned by the recently reinstated King Charles II, the Royal Observatory remains in operation on the south bank of the Thames to this day.
15. A. Russia. The so-called Russo-Turkish War lasted for the next five years.
16. D. The Netherlands. The revolution led to the English king James II (who was jointly James VII of Scotland) being ousted from the throne in November 1688, and replaced by his daughter, Queen Mary II, and her Dutch husband, William III of Orange (who was also James' nephew). England became a constitutional monarchy as a result.
17. C. 1692.
18. A. Ireland. Also known as the Williamite War, the War of the Two Kings was a direct consequence of England's Glorious Revolution, with forces loyal to both James II of England and his Dutch usurper William of Orange, William III, clashing in over two years of war. Ireland - which had fallen under English rule during the Tudors - proved a fierce battleground in the aftermath of the revolution, as James II had been Catholic while both William and his wife Queen Mary were Protestant. As in England, the Williamite forces eventually proved victorious.

DID YOU KNOW?

Shakespeare's final play, *The Tempest*, is thought to have been based on a real-life shipwreck that had taken place in 1609.

14.
SOUTH AMERICAN HISTORY

Much like its northern cousin, South America saw thousands of years of indigenous history become disrupted by European explorers, conquistadors, and settlers from the 15th century onward. Since then, the continent's 13 nations - from Brazil (the largest) to French Guiana (the smallest, an overseas territory of France) - have established themselves as some of the world's most culturally and politically exciting countries. So, let's see how much you know about the history of this most extraordinary of continents.

1. The little-known Caral civilization emerged in South America at roughly the same time as Ancient Egypt, around 3500 BCE - in what modern-day country?

    a. Peru
    b. Chile
    c. Argentina
    d. Brazil

2. True or false: The native South Americans domesticated llamas and alpacas in the Andes before horses were domesticated in the West.

3. The Nazca people who flourished in Peru for almost 1,000 years, from the 1st century BCE onward, are known for producing what in the middle of the Peruvian desert?

    a. Canals
    b. Cave
    c. Stone geoglyphs' artwork
    d. Manmade lakes

4. Thought to have been founded sometime around 100 CE, the ancient city of Tiwanaku - which was once home to more than 10,000 people - lies beside what major South American landmark?

    a. Lake Titicaca
    b. The River Amazon
    c. Angel Falls
    d. Sugarloaf Mountain

5. In what century did the Catholic church instigate a series of Papal Bulls that gave European missionaries religious permission to take

possession of non-Christian lands around the world, leading to Spain and Portugal's colonization of South America?

    a. 13th century
    b. 14th century
    c. 15th century
    d. 16th century

6. What city was named the first capital of Brazil in 1534, remaining the country's chief city for more than 200 years?

    a. São Paulo
    b. Salvador
    c. Recife
    d. Belém

7. What Peruvian city was once the capital of the Incan Empire?

    a. Cuzco
    b. Lima
    c. Cajamarca
    d. Arequipa

8. True or false: No historical records or contemporary accounts will ever be found in the ancient city of Machu Picchu - because the Incan people had no written language.

9. When the Italian explorer Amerigo Vespucci arrived off the coast of Suriname in 1499, where did he think he was?

    a. Asia
    b. Greenland
    c. Australia
    d. Africa

10. The Incan emperor Huayna Capac died of what in 1527?

    a. Caiman bite
    b. Smallpox
    c. Wildfire
    d. Tainted food

11. Colonists and invaders from what European country sacked the capital of the Incan Empire in 1533?

a. England
b. The Netherlands
c. Italy
d. Spain

12. In what South American nation were rival English, Dutch, and French colonies established in the 1630s - making it the only country in South America to have English as its official language today?

a. Chile
b. Guyana
c. Colombia
d. Argentina

13. What South American archipelago was discovered by Western explorers in 1690?

a. Galapagos Islands
b. Trinidad and Tobago
c. The Falkland Islands
d. Easter Island

14. What South American nation and its capital were destroyed by a devastating earthquake and tsunami in 1746?

a. Peru
b. Brazil
c. Suriname
d. Venezuela

15. True or false: The country of Venezuela is named after the city of Venice because early European explorers to the area thought the natives' coastal stilted houses looked like the buildings lining the canals there.

16. In what South American city was the revolutionary Simón Bolívar born in 1783?

a. Rio de Janeiro
b. Quito
c. Lima
d. Caracas

17. In 1947, Norwegian explorer and adventurer Thor Heyerdahl set sail from South America attempting to cross what body of water single-handedly in a hand-built raft?

    a. Southern Ocean
    b. Atlantic Ocean
    c. Caribbean Sea
    d. Pacific Ocean

18. Which two nations went to war for 10 weeks in 1982 in a dispute over the ownership of South America's Falkland Islands?

SOLUTIONS

1. A. Peru. Also known as the Caral-Supe or Norte Chico civilization, the Caral people's network of cities scattered across northern Peru is now recognized as the oldest known civilization in the Americas.
2. False. Roughly 1,000 years is thought to separate the domestication of horses, around 6,000 years ago, and the domestication of South America's camelid creatures, around 3000 BCE.
3. C. Stone geoglyphs artwork. Archaeologists and anthropologists have long debated the purpose of the so-called Nazca Lines, which are now recognized as a UNESCO World Heritage Site. The prevailing theory today is that these gigantic images and networks of stone lines were created by the Nazca people so that they could be seen by their culture's sky deities.
4. A. Lake Titicaca.
5. C. 15th century. Although the earliest of these papal rulings were concerned with Europe's colonies in West Africa, the *Inter caetera* established by Pope Alexander VI in 1493 explicitly recognized Spain and Portugal's territorial claims in the Americas.
6. B. Salvador.
7. A. Cuzco.
8. True.
9. A. Asia. Believing he had arrived in eastern Asia, Vespucci inaccurately thought that if he were able to sail around the southernmost cape of South America, he would reach the Indian Ocean.
10. B. Smallpox. Huayna Capac was one of the first and most important figures of the early Americas to succumb to a disease inadvertently introduced by European colonists.
11. D. Spain. Led by explorer Francisco Pizzaro, the Spanish sacked the Incan Empire and - despite agreeing to pay the ransom demanded of him - murdered the Incan emperor Atahualpa.
12. B. Guyana.
13. C. The Falkland Islands. Discovered by mariner John Strong, the islands were named in honor of Viscount Falkland, who was the treasurer of the British Royal Navy at the time.
14. A. Peru. The so-called Lima–Callao earthquake of 1746 is thought to have had a magnitude of 8.8.
15. True.

16. D. Caracas.
17. D. Pacific Ocean. Heyerdahl successfully sailed his raft, the *Kon-Tiki*, more than 5,000 miles from the coast of Peru to the Tuamotu Islands in Polynesia. In doing so, he proved that the ancient peoples of South America could have carried out the same voyage, and thereby colonized the islands of the Pacific.
18. Argentina and the UK.

DID YOU KNOW?

The Portuguese royal family moved to Brazil in 1807.

15.
COMING TO AMERICA

Although it's mostly associated with the likes of Plymouth Rock and Jamestown, the history of the European exploration and colonization of North America dates back around 1,000 years to the early Viking explorations of the Arctic. The arrival of Christopher Columbus in 1492, as well as later explorers like John Cabot and Juan Ponce de Léon further led to the settlement of North America, more than a century before the arrival of the Pilgrim Fathers in the early 1600s. Time to test what you know!

1. In what North American nation did Columbus make his first landfall in the Americas on October 12, 1492?

   a. Cuba
   b. United States
   c. Jamaica
   d. The Bahamas

2. In 1473, the Portuguese mariner João Vaz Corte-Real wrote in his journal that he had traveled to the "land of codfish" off the coast of North America. Where do historians now believe he may have landed?

   a. Manhattan
   b. Bermuda
   c. Newfoundland
   d. Greenland

3. Long before Europeans arrived in what is now the United States, European settlers established what Caribbean capital in 1496?

   a. Santo Domingo
   b. Nassau
   c. Kingston
   d. Havana

4. Founded in 1570, the Ajacán Mission was an attempt by Spain to establish a Jesuit missionary settlement in what modern-day state of the USA?

   a. Florida
   b. Louisiana
   c. South Carolina
   d. Virginia

5. In what US state is Roanoke Island, the site of a failed English colony established by Sir Walter Raleigh in 1585?

    a. Delaware
    b. Georgia
    c. Maryland
    d. North Carolina

6. Which European country founded the colonial region of Acadia northeastern North America in 1604?

    a. France
    b. The Netherlands
    c. Spain
    d. Sweden

7. In what part of North America did England establish the early settlement of Cuper's Cove in 1610, three years after the foundation of Jamestown, Virginia?

    a. Newfoundland
    b. Baffin Island
    c. Florida Keys
    d. Cape Cod

8. What was the name of the Pilgrim Fathers' second ship, which after leaving Plymouth in 620 alongside the *Mayflower* was found to be unseaworthy and abandoned in Holland?

    a. Groundswell
    b. Speedwell
    c. Overswell
    d. Farewell

9. The Battle of the Plains of Abraham, fought between British and French forces in 1759, took place outside the walls of which major colonial city?

    a. Quebec
    b. Montreal
    c. St. John's
    d. Salem

10. What proportion of the population of Jamestown died shortly after it was founded in the winter of 1609–10?

    a. 5%
    b. 25%
    c. 55%
    d. 85%

11. On what island was Britain's first permanent Caribbean colony established in 1624?

    a. Dominica
    b. Aruba
    c. St. Kitts
    d. Key Largo

12. Cape Breton Island, off the coast of Nova Scotia, was an early attempt by what nation to establish a North American colony?

    a. Scotland
    b. Sicily
    c. Venice
    d. Austria-Hungary

13. Founded in 1638, Fort Christina was which European country's first North American colony?

    a. Italy
    b. Sweden
    c. Denmark
    d. Poland

14. In what decade was Salem, Massachusetts founded?

    a. 1610s
    b. 1620s
    c. 1640s
    d. 1660s

15. What Canadian city was founded in 1642 as a French settlement named Ville-Marie, or "Mary's Town"?

    a. Montreal
    b. Toronto

c. Vancouver

d. Halifax

16. True or false: The cities of Detroit and Mobile were both founded by French settlers.

17. What major US city was founded in the summer of 1729, when the Governor of Maryland officially signed an act permitting the construction of a new town "on the North side of the Patapsco River"?

a. Annapolis

b. Baltimore

c. Laurel

d. Cambridge

18. What US city was founded by Spain in 1706 and named after the then Viceroy of New Spain, the vast colonial region controlled by Spain for over 300 years?

a. Albuquerque

b. Pensacola

c. San Antonio

d. Tucson

SOLUTIONS

1. D. The Bahamas.
2. C. Newfoundland.
3. A. Santo Domingo. The capital of the Dominican Republic, Santo Domingo is credited with being the first European permanent settlement and remains the oldest continuously inhabited European settlement in the Americas.
4. D. Virginia. Predating the founding of Jamestown by over three decades, the Ajacán Mission proved a disaster when almost the entire population was massacred by the local native peoples after less than a year in February 1571.
5. D. North Carolina. Five years after its founding, a vessel arriving in Roanoke in 1590 found it deserted. The fates of the 120 or so colonists known to have lived there at the time remain a mystery.
6. A. France. Arcadia was eventually conquered by the British in 1713.
7. A. Newfoundland.
8. B. Speedwell.
9. A. Quebec. Also known simply as the Battle of Quebec, the outcome of the Battle of the Plains of Abraham - with the British defeating the local French forces - eventually proved significant in the founding and eventual independence of Canada.
10. D. 85%. Known as the Starving Time, the disastrous winter of 1609 left just 61 people alive in Jamestown by the spring; the previous year, the population had been around 500.
11. C. St. Kitts.
12. A. Scotland. Scotland's settlement on Cape Breton in Nova Scotia was founded in 1625; the name Nova Scotia itself, meanwhile, literally means "New Scotland."
13. B. Sweden. Located around one mile outside Wilmington, Delaware, Fort Christina was named after the reigning Swedish monarch at the time, Queen Christina.
14. B. 1620s. Salem was founded by the English in 1626.
15. A. Montreal. Originally named for the Virgin Mary, the city is thought to have been later renamed in honor of the nearby Mont Royal, a large hill at its center.

16. True.
17. B. Baltimore.
18. A. Albuquerque. The city was named in honor of Francisco Fernández de la Cueva, the 10th Duke of Albuquerque - which at the time was a major title in the Spanish nobility.

DID YOU KNOW?

The *Mayflower* was ill-designed for oceanic travel, and its bulky shape meant that a voyage that should have taken a month ended up taking twice as long.

16.
WARS & BATTLES

There's a wise old saying that claims history is written by the victors, which means an awful lot of what we know and understand about the past is based on the outcomes of wars, battles, and military clashes. Covering more than 2,500 years of history, let's test your knowledge of just that with these questions dedicated to the wars of the past.

1. Who were the Ancient Greeks' opponents in the famous Battle of Marathon in 490 BCE?

    a. Romans
    b. Persians
    c. Egyptians
    d. Hittites

2. Which famous Greek general was one of the central figures in the ancient Peloponnesian Wars between Athens and Sparta?

    a. Pericles
    b. Leonidas
    c. Patrocles
    d. Menelaus

3. In what country did a series of clashes known as the Red Eyebrows Rebellion occur in the 1st century CE?

    a. Russia
    b. China
    c. Spain
    d. England

4. True or false: The Mayans fought a series of decisive civil wars between rival states during the time of their empire that have become known as Star Wars.

5. In 1066 - just days before the more famous Battle of Hastings - the English army fought a second battle in which a claim to the English throne was made by an outsider. What was the name of the battle?

    a. Stamford Bridge
    b. Culloden
    c. Hedgeley Moor
    d. Losecoat Field

6. In which European country did the so-called Loon War take place in the 1200s?

    a. Norway
    b. The Netherlands
    c. Ireland
    d. Austria

7. Which medieval English king fought the Barons' War from 1215–1217?

    a. William I
    b. Stephen
    c. Richard I
    d. John

8. During Europe's long-lasting Hundred Years' War, which of these ancient kingdoms fought on the same side as the English?

    a. Scotland
    b. Aragon
    c. Castile
    d. Portugal

9. Which of these is the name of a genuine war that broke out between the rival Spanish kingdoms of Castile and Aragon in the 14th century?

    a. The War of the two Annas
    b. The War of the two Charles
    c. The War of the two Peters
    d. The War of the two Catherines

10. Symbolized by a white rose, which English dynasty was the opponent of the House of Lancaster - symbolized by a red rose - during the Wars of the Roses in the 15th century?

    a. Cornwall
    b. York
    c. Norfolk
    d. Kent

11. Europe's Eighty Years' War, fought from 1568–1648, secured which country's independence from Spain?

    a. The Netherlands

b. Denmark

c. Austria

d. Morocco

12. Which two ancient rivals fought the Bishops' Wars of the 17th century?

a. England and Scotland

b. Spain and Portugal

c. Greece and Rome

d. China and Japan

13. In what century was the so-called War of the Spanish Succession fought?

a. 16th century

b. 17th century

c. 18th century

d. 19th century

14. Who were Great Britain's opponents in the infamous War of Jenkins' Ear in the mid-1700s?

a. Spain

b. Russia

c. France

d. Ottoman Empire

15. In what state were the first shots fired during the American Revolutionary War in 1775?

a. Maryland

b. Virginia

c. Delaware

d. Massachusetts

16. True or false: France and Mexico went to war in 1838 over damage to a restaurant.

17. The Battle of Palmito Ranch is often claimed to have been the final encounter in which 19th-century conflict?

a. American Civil War

b. War of 1812

c. Crimean War

d. Boer War

18. Who was the US President during World War I, who led the United States into the conflict in 1917?

a. Theodore Roosevelt
b. William Howard Taft
c. Woodrow Wilson
d. Warren G Harding

SOLUTIONS

1. B. Persians. The Battle of Marathon - after which the running race is famously named - was the end of the Persian king Darius I's first attempt to conquer Greece.
2. A. Pericles. Fought in the mid-1st millennium BCE, the Peloponnesian Wars were fought between the two Greek superstates of Athens and Sparta - as well as their surrounding allies - over control of the Greek world.
3. B. China. The rebellion was so named because the uprisers painted their eyebrows red.
4. True! The term refers to a symbol or glyph used to represent the time of conflict in the Mayan writing system, which resembles a star.
5. A. Stamford Bridge. The battle saw the newly crowned King Harold Godwinson successfully see off an attempt to claim the throne by the Norwegian King Harald Hardrada at the town of Stamford Bridge in Yorkshire. Just three weeks later, Harold's exhausted and depleted armies were forced to march to the other end of his kingdom to fight at Hastings, where he was defeated by William the Conqueror.
6. B. The Netherlands. The war was fought between two rival successors, one of whom was Count Louis of Loon, or Loeën - the name of a county in the Holy Roman Empire.
7. D. John. War broke out in the aftermath of the signing of the Magna Carta in 1215, after King John waged a disastrous war against the King of France, much to the displeasure of the landowners or barons of his kingdom.
8. D. Portugal. Portugal is popularly known as "England's oldest ally" - the two countries signed Europe's oldest known peace treaty, the Treaty of Windsor, in 1386 and have been allied ever since.
9. C. The War of the Two Peters. The war was fought by the rival kings Peter of Castile and Peter IV of Aragon.
10. B. York.
11. A. The Netherlands.
12. A. England and Scotland. The wars were the result of King Charles I's attempt to impose Anglican church services on the churches of Scotland.
13. C. 18th century. 1701–1714.

14. A. Spain. The war was sparked by Captain Robert Jenkins, who claimed in England's House of Commons that his ear had been cut off by Spanish privateers in the Caribbean.
15. D. Massachusetts. Although accounts differ, it is generally believed the first shots were fired at Lexington, Massachusetts.
16. True. The so-called Pastry War - sparked by the claim of a French pastry chef working in Mexico that some Mexican army officers had damaged his restaurant - lasted over a year.
17. A. American Civil War.
18. C. Woodrow Wilson.

DID YOU KNOW?

The marathon race is famously named after the Battle of Marathon after a soldier ran from the battlefield to Athens - so the first person to run the marathon was the soldier, Pheidippides!

17.
THE 1700S

The 18th century was a period of great upheaval around the world. Many of the world's greatest empires and states were beginning to crumble as their members and colonies strove for independence. Mutual belligerence between many nations remained significant, and near-constant wars and rebellions broke out across the globe. But against this tumultuous backdrop, scientists and inventors started to make the kinds of advances that would pave the way for the Industrial Revolution. After the 1700s, it's fair to say, the world would never quite be the same; but how much do you know of that era?

1. The Ako Vendetta - in which a band of 48 *ronin* fighters brutally avenged the death of their master - famously took place in what country in 1702?

    a. Turkey
    b. Japan
    c. Russia
    d. Finland

2. Which Russian city was founded by the tsar in 1703, and remained the country's capital until 1918?

    a. Minsk
    b. St. Petersburg
    c. Omsk
    d. Karaganda

3. The 1707 Act of Union officially merged which two nations together?

    a. England and Scotland
    b. Czechia and Slovakia
    c. Austria and Hungary
    d. Spain and Portugal

4. In 1717, Britain and France agreed to ally their forces against Spain by signing the Triple Alliance - alongside which other European country?

    a. Denmark
    b. Germany
    c. The Netherlands
    d. Italy

5. Which famous pirate was killed off the coast of North Carolina in 1718?

a. Blackbeard

b. Anne Bonny

c. Calico Jack

d. Redbeard

6. What Christian faith was founded in the late 1720s by John Wesley?

   a. Anabaptism

   b. Quakerism

   c. Mormonism

   d. Methodism

7. In 1742, Marvel's Mill in Northampton, England, became the first water-powered…what?

   a. Printing press

   b. Cotton mill

   c. Farmyard plow

   d. Sewing machine

8. Which country made two unsuccessful attempts to invade Britain in 1744 and 1759?

   a. Norway

   b. Russia

   c. France

   d. Prussia

9. A prolonged 400–500-year period of noticeably cold weather in the North Atlantic region reached its peak in the middle of the 18th century. What is this period now known as?

   a. The Long Chill

   b. The Freezer Box

   c. The Arctic Blast

   d. The Little Ice Age

10. Which European capital was devastated by a gigantic earthquake and tsunami in 1755?

    a. Rome

    b. Lisbon

    c. London

    d. Copenhagen

11. True or false: When King George III came to power in England in 1760, he was the first English king to speak English as his first language for almost 50 years.

12. Which of these famous composers was both born in and died in the 1700s?

    a. Mozart
    b. Puccini
    c. Chopin
    d. Bach

13. Who ruled Russia from 1762 to 1796?

    a. Ivan the Terrible
    b. Nicholas I
    c. Empress Elizabeth
    d. Catherine the Great

14. Which famous explorer traveled around and mapped Australia and New Zealand in a two-year voyage from 1769–70?

    a. Henry Cabot
    b. Vitus Bering
    c. George Vancouver
    d. James Cook

15. In which US city did British troops fire wildly into a crowd of protesters on March 5, 1770, in one of the most infamous events in the leadup to the American Revolution?

    a. Baltimore
    b. New York
    c. Concord
    d. Boston

16. Invented by the Montgolfier Brothers, what early mode of transport was first demonstrated in Paris in 1783?

    a. Hot air balloon
    b. Hovercraft
    c. Microlite
    d. Tandem bicycle

17. What was the name of the Treaty that officially ended the American Revolutionary War in 1783?

    a. Treaty of London
    b. Treaty of Brussels
    c. Treaty of Rome
    d. Treaty of Paris

18. In 1796, the English scientist Edward Jenner produced the world's first vaccine. What disease was it used to combat?

    a. Yellow fever
    b. Measles
    c. Smallpox
    d. Polio

SOLUTIONS

1. B. Japan.
2. B. St. Petersburg. The city - still one of Russia's largest - was founded by Tsar Peter the Great. It was later renamed Petrograd, and then Leningrad after Lenin's death in 1924, before its original name was restored shortly before the fall of the USSR in 1991.
3. A. England and Scotland. The Act took effect on May 1, creating the Kingdom of Great Britain.
4. C. The Netherlands. Against a backdrop of increasing military tensions across Europe, the three great nations of Britain, France, and the Dutch Republic (as it was at the time) agreed to join to see off the threat of Spain becoming a superpower. The Triple Alliance became the Quadruple Alliance the following year when Austria agreed to join as well.
5. A. Blackbeard. AKA Edward Teach, Blackbeard was English by birth but chiefly operated in the waters off the coast of America and in the Caribbean.
6. D. Methodism. Founded at Oxford University, by both John Wesley and his younger brother Charles, Methodism originally stressed the importance of a strict "methodical" approach to religious life and study.
7. B. Cotton mill. Situated on rural England's river Nene, the mill was not only the first water-powered cotton mill in the world but also the first powered by an inanimate power source.
8. C. France. The 1744 invasion was held back and partly wrecked by storms and high swells in the English Channel. A second invasion in 1759, involving 100,000 French troops and aimed at ending Britain's involvement in the Seven Years' War, was called off even before it began.
9. D. The Little Ice Age. Though not a true ice age in the ecological sense, the Little Ice Age is said to have lasted from around the 15th to the 19th century (with some estimates suggesting it may even have begun in the 1300s). Various explanations have been put forward to account for this sudden and noticeable dip in temperatures in the northern hemisphere, from an increase in volcanic activity to reduced solar

radiation, shifting sea currents, and minute variations in the Earth's axis.

10. B. Lisbon. The Portuguese capital had already been destroyed twice before by earthquakes, in 1321 and 1531, when a third enormous quake struck in the 18th century. The 1755 Lisbon earthquake was one of the deadliest in world history, with 12,000 killed.

11. True! The House of Hanover, based in Germany, rose to claim the English throne under King George I in 1714. Both he and his successor George II (1727–60) spoke English as their first language.

12. A. Mozart. Born in 1685, Bach died in 1755 - the year before Mozart was born in Salzburg, Austria, in 1756. He died (in somewhat unresolved circumstances) at the age of just 35, in 1791.

13. D. Catherine the Great. Catherine swept to power as empress of Russia having overthrown her husband, Peter III.

14. D. James Cook.

15. D. Boston. The so-called Boston Massacre led to the deaths of five American colonists; of the nine British troops involved, just two were convicted of murder and were branded on their thumbs as punishment.

16. A. Hot air balloon. Although it had been suggested the first hot air balloon flight be tested for safety by two convicted criminals, in the end, a sheep, a duck, and a rooster were the first passengers.

17. D. Treaty of Paris.

18. C. Smallpox.

DID YOU KNOW?

Queen Anne was so sick and bloated by the time of her death, she had to be buried in a square coffin that was carried to her grave by 14 men.

18.
EUROPEAN HISTORY

With so many peoples and cultures packed so tightly into a relatively small landmass, the history of Europe is long and tumultuous, with endlessly shifting borders and countless wars and skirmishes. And what's more, because this long history is so well documented and preserved in the historical record, much of what has happened in Europe over the last few millennia is widely known, studied, and discussed. Let's test your knowledge of precisely that, with this quiz all about this most eventful continent's past.

1. Dating back to the Stone Age, some of the world's oldest cave paintings can be found in Chauvet Cave in what European country?

    a. Ireland
    b. Sweden
    c. Greece
    d. France

2. Developed in Greece sometime in the middle of the 2nd millennium BCE, Linear B is the name given to an early form of what?

    a. Musical notation
    b. Written language
    c. Zodiac
    d. Battle formation

3. Thespis was the name of a famous figure from Ancient Greece, who is known as the world's first...what?

    a. Cook
    b. Poet
    c. Dancer
    d. Actor

4. The Picts were an early tribe of ancient Europeans, who chiefly lived where?

    a. Scotland
    b. Denmark
    c. Poland
    d. Italy

5. True or false: Although known for their architectural endeavors, Europe's river Danube proved too difficult to bridge, leading the Romans never to construct a permanent crossing.

6. What European island was invaded by the Arabs in 827 and remained an Islamic emirate state for the next 250 years?

    a. Corfu
    b. Cyprus
    c. Sicily
    d. Corsica

7. By what epithet was the ancient English king Ethelred known?

    a. Undressed
    b. Unattractive
    c. Unliked
    d. Unready

8. Which of these is famously depicted on the Bayeux Tapestry, showing the events of the Norman Conquest and the Battle of Hastings?

    a. A whirlpool
    b. A comet
    c. A tornado
    d. An avalanche

9. In 1238, work began on the famous Alhambra palace in which Spanish city?

    a. Barcelona
    b. Bilbao
    c. Malaga
    d. Granada

10. Although a similar structure has stood on the same site since Roman times, the current Ponte Vecchio in Florence was built in the mid-1300s. But what is it?

    a. Church
    b. Bridge
    c. Stadium
    d. Crypt

11. Which English king famously fought at the Battle of Agincourt in 1415 - which was later dramatized by William Shakespeare?

    a. John
    b. Richard II
    c. Henry V
    d. Henry VIII

12. Later as a financier of Columbus' voyage to America, what was the name of the 15th-century Queen of Castille whose marriage to King Ferdinand of Aragon united the two Spanish crowns in 1469?

    a. Katherina
    b. Isabella
    c. Donatella
    d. Maria

13. In the English 16th century, the English writer and printer William Tyndale famously translated what book into English for the first time?

    a. *Don Quixote*
    b. *Ovid's Metamorphoses*
    c. *The Iliad*
    d. *The Bible*

14. Which European country established the trading colony of Macao, on the south coast of China, in 1557?

    a. England
    b. Portugal
    c. The Netherlands
    d. Italy

15. What happened to Shakespeare's famous Globe Theatre in London during a performance of his play *Henry VIII* in 1613?

    a. It burned down
    b. It flooded
    c. The roof collapsed
    d. The audience rioted

16. What famous European museum was founded by Catherine the Great in 1764?

a. The Hermitage
b. The Louvre
c. The British Museum
d. The Rijksmuseum

17. What name is given to the series of brutal massacres that took place during the First Republic of France, as part of the French Revolution?

    a. The Rule of Horror
    b. The Law of Dread
    c. The Management of Panic
    d. The Reign of Terror

18. In what year did the Titanic sink?

    a. 1902
    b. 1912
    c. 1922
    d. 1932

SOLUTIONS

1. D. France. Images in the Chauvet Cave, near Avignon, include hunted animals, horses, and handprints.
2. B. Written language. Linear B is an early syllabic script that was used to write Mycenean Greek, the earliest written form of the Greek language.
3. D. Actor. Hence actors today are known as *thespians*.
4. A. Scotland.
5. False. Although the Romans are known to have used non-permanent pontoon bridges to cross certain rivers that had rougher currents, they built at least two Danube crossings - one of which, Trajan's Bridge close to the Romanian–Serbian border, is thought to have been the longest bridge in the world for at least 1,000 years.
6. C. Sicily. Known as the Emirate of Sicily, or Fatimid Sicily, several attempts to reclaim the island were made by Byzantine and Norman mercenaries in the 11th century, but it remained under Arab control until 1091.
7. D. Unready. Properly known as Ethelred II, he reigned over ancient England in two periods, first from 978 to 1013, and then again from 1014 until his death in 1016. Contrary to its modern meaning, the epithet Unready does not mean unprepared, but in Old English essentially meant ill-advised.
8. B. A comet. Halley's Comet is visible for only a brief period, roughly every 75–79 years. We know now that it would have been visible in England in the spring of 1066, and ultimately the trailing star shown on the Bayeux Tapestry is now believed to be a depiction of it.
9. D. Granada.
10. B. Bridge.
11. C. Henry V. Shakespeare's famous St Crispin's Day speech (which includes the line, "We few, we happy few, we band of brothers") is spoken at the battle in Act IV of *Henry V*.
12. B. Isabella.
13. D. The Bible. Strictly speaking, Tyndale's Bible was not the first attempt at an English translation (as Old English texts had been produced many years earlier), and nor was it complete. But it was the first translation to work directly from the original Hebrew and Greek, plus it was mass-produced in such numbers that it soon proved a landmark achievement.

Tyndale's work saw him fall foul of England's strict heresy laws at the time, however, and he, having fled to Europe, was eventually captured, and executed in 1536.

14. B. Portugal. The territory remained under Portuguese control until 1999.
15. A. It burned down. It is thought the Globe's roof caught fire when a spark from a stage cannon ignited the straw thatch.
16. A. The Hermitage.
17. D. The Reign of Terror.
18. B. 1912. The *Titanic* is said to have sunk at around 2:20 a.m. on the morning of April 15, 1912.

DID YOU KNOW?

More than 100,000 people watched the *Titanic* launch from its dockyard in Belfast on March 31, 1911.

19.
THE FOUNDING FATHERS

America's Founding Fathers were the late 18th-century leaders of the Revolutionary Era who oversaw the union of America's original Thirteen Colonies, the War of Independence from Great Britain, and the establishment of a new United States government. Quite who counts as a Founding Father and who does not is open to some debate, but in general terms, the phrase is typically taken to refer to the recorded signatories of the United States Declaration of Independence, the Articles of Confederation, and the United States Constitution, alongside a handful of other important documents - and other important historical figures. How much do you remember about these pivotal figures in America's past?

1. Whose name is famously written the largest on the Declaration of Independence, taking up a full six square inches of space on the paper?

    a. Samuel Chase
    b. John Adam
    c. James Wilson
    d. John Hancock

2. Benjamin Franklin once admitted he wasn't a fan of using the bald eagle as the emblem of America. Which avian did he prefer instead?

    a. Mockingbird
    b. Robin
    c. Turkey
    d. Stork

3. Which of the Founding Fathers wrote the original draft version of the Declaration of Independence?

    a. Thomas Jefferson
    b. Robert Treat Paine
    c. John Witherspoon
    d. Josiah Bartlett

4. True or false: The first draft of the US Declaration of Independence included a clause seeking to prohibit the sale of alcohol.

5. Which of the Founding Fathers founded the New York Post in 1801?

    a. Benjamin Franklin
    b. Alexander Hamilton
    c. Thomas Jefferson

d.   Thomas McKean

6.   What did John Adams once refer to as the "most insignificant office that ever the invention of man contrived"?

   a.   Attorney General
   b.   President
   c.   Vice President
   d.   Speaker of the House of Representatives

7.   Which signatory of the Declaration of Independence served as the first governor of New Hampshire?

   a.   William Whipple
   b.   Josiah Bartlett
   c.   Stephen Hopkins
   d.   Arthur Middleton

8.   A well-known party hostess on the Washington social scene, what was the name of Founding Father James Madison's wife?

   a.   Molley
   b.   Dolley
   c.   Holley
   d.   Sally

9.   Founding Father Albert Gallatin emigrated to the United States in the 1780s, eventually rising through the political ranks to serve under four early presidents as America's longest-serving Secretary of the Treasury. But where was he born?

   a.   Switzerland
   b.   Sweden
   c.   New Zealand
   d.   Italy

10.   What unlikely gift did Zebulon Pike give Thomas Jefferson in 1807?

   a.   Two raccoons
   b.   Two rattlesnakes
   c.   Two alligators
   d.   Two bear cubs

11. In the 1790s, which of the Founding Fathers became embroiled in a scandal called the Reynolds Affair?

    a. Alexander Hamilton
    b. Benjamin Franklin
    c. Elbridge Gerry
    d. Button Gwinnett

12. Where was Paul Revere born?

    a. Washington
    b. Concord
    c. Boston
    d. New York

13. True or false: John Adams and Thomas Jefferson died on the same day.

14. After he left the presidency after two full terms, what did George Washington enjoy doing in his retirement?

    a. Sewing samplers
    b. Growing herbs
    c. Distilling whiskey
    d. Throwing pots

15. No one in the Revolutionary Era is thought to have used the phrase "founding father" themselves. The term wasn't used in the context of America until 1916 - by which future US President?

    a. Warren G Harding
    b. Lyndon B Johnson
    c. Dwight D Eisenhower
    d. Calvin Coolidge

16. How were Founding Fathers John Adams and Samuel Adams related?

    a. Brothers
    b. Brothers-in-law
    c. Uncle and nephew
    d. Second cousins

17. How many people signed BOTH the Declaration of Independence and the US Constitution?

a. One
b. Two
c. Three
d. Six

18. And who was the only person to sign all four great founding state papers of the United States - the Continental Association, the US Declaration of Independence, the Articles of Confederation, and the Constitution?

a. Rufus King
b. Thomas Jefferson
c. Roger Sherman
d. Abraham Baldwin

SOLUTIONS

1. D. John Hancock. Hence Hancock's name has since become a slang term for a person's signature or handwritten name.
2. C. Turkey.
3. A. Thomas Jefferson. Jefferson was considered the best writer of the group, and so he was given the task of drawing up the first draft.
4. False. Though Jefferson did add in an early clause outlawing slavery but removed it when he and others feared it would cause contention among delegates from southern states.
5. B. Alexander Hamilton. Originally, it was the *New York Evening Post*. It remains one of America's longest continually published newspapers.
6. C. Vice President. George Washington might have made him his VP, but Adams himself wasn't a fan of the role or the title!
7. B. Josiah Bartlett.
8. B. Dolley. As First Lady from 1809 to 1817, Dolley put her legendary party-hosting skills to good use, holding functions to which members of both political parties were invited, in the interests of achieving bipartisan collaboration.
9. A. Switzerland. Gallatin was born in Geneva, and he became affectionately known as "America's Swiss Founding Father."
10. D. Two bear cubs. Jefferson later wrote that although he appreciated the gift, the bears were "too dangerous and troublesome for me to keep."
11. A. Alexander Hamilton. While serving in the US treasury in 1791, Hamilton had an affair with a married woman, Maria Reynolds.
12. C. Boston. Revere was born in the North End neighborhood of Boston in 1734.
13. True. Stranger still, that day was July 4.
14. C. Distilling whiskey. Washington opened a whiskey distillery at Mount Vernon in 1797.
15. A. Warren G Harding. While still serving as a Senator of Ohio, Harding used the phrase in a speech in 1916.
16. D. Second cousins.
17. D. Six. Only six Founding Fathers signed both the Declaration of Independence and the Constitution, namely George Clymer, Benjamin

Franklin, Robert Morris, George Read, James Wilson, and Roger Sherman.

18. C. Roger Sherman

DID YOU KNOW?

There is no mention of Thomas Jefferson's presidency on his grave.

20.
DISASTERS AND CATASTROPHES

History is the recording of events of note, of course, and few things are more noteworthy than grand disasters, catastrophes, tragedies, and calamities. Covering more than two millennia of history, how many of these questions dedicated to history's more extraordinary calamities can you answer?

1. Completed in the 3rd century BCE, which of the Seven Wonders of the Ancient world was destroyed by a series of earthquakes, and eventually demolished altogether in the late 1400s?

    a. Pharos of Alexandria
    b. Hanging Gardens of Babylon
    c. Colossus of Rhodes
    d. Temple of Artemis

2. The eruption of which volcano destroyed the city of Pompeii in 79 CE?

    a. Stromboli
    b. Etna
    c. Vesuvius
    d. Lipari

3. In the mid-6th century CE, an immense landside created a devastating mini tsunami wholly contained inside what lake?

    a. Lake Baikal
    b. Lake Geneva
    c. Lake Superior
    d. Lake Victoria

4. In 1091, the original wooden London Bridge on the Thames in central London was destroyed by what freak weather event?

    a. Tornado
    b. Tsunami
    c. Avalanche
    d. Hailstorm

5. The so-called *White Ship* disaster of 1120 killed so many members of which country's royal line of succession that it was thrown into a brief civil war.

    a. France
    b. England

c. Sweden

d. Japan

6. In 1287, an immense flood overwhelmed which European country, killing more than 50,000 people?

a. Ireland

b. The Netherlands

c. Portugal

d. Denmark

7. True or false: When the Indonesian volcano Krakatoa erupted in 1883, the sound of the explosion was heard 2,000 miles away in Australia.

8. The deadliest natural disaster in US history was the Great Storm of 1900, chiefly focused on the area around what coastal city?

a. Galveston

b. Biloxi

c. Baton Rouge

d. Tampa

9. In 1906, the French town of Courrières was devastated by a disaster affecting what industry?

a. Brewing

b. Mining

c. Shipbuilding

d. Oil drilling

10. In what European city was the *Titanic*'s last landfall before it embarked across the Atlantic Ocean?

a. Southampton

b. Cherbourg

c. Belfast

d. Queenstown

11. White Friday is the name given to a natural disaster that struck the Italian Front of World War I in 1916. What was it?

a. Forest fire

b. Flood

c. Earthquake

d. Avalanche

12. In what US city were 21 people killed by a flood of molasses in 1919?

    a. Minneapolis
    b. Philadelphia
    c. Des Moines
    d. Boston

13. An estimated 4,000,000 people were killed by a flood affecting one of the largest river networks in which country in 1931?

    a. China
    b. Russia
    c. Brazil
    d. Sudan

14. In 1960, the strongest earthquake in recorded history - reaching a magnitude of 9.5 - struck the town of Valdivia, in what country?

    a. Italy
    b. Chile
    c. Nepal
    d. New Zealand

15. In what year of the 20th century did more than 140 tornadoes touch down in Canada and the United States within 24 hours, causing what was at the time the worst "super outbreak" in North American history?

    a. 1914
    b. 1934
    c. 1954
    d. 1974

16. In what country did Typhoon Nina cause the collapse of the immense Banqiao Dam in 1975, resulting in more than 25,000 fatalities?

    a. China
    b. Indonesia
    c. Sri Lanka
    d. Somalia

17. The world's worst industrial accident occurred at a Union Carbide pesticide plant in Bhopal in 1984, in which Asian country?

    a. Thailand

b. South Korea
c. India
d. Afghanistan

18. In 1995, the Soufrière Hills volcano on which Caribbean island erupted; eventually leaving half the island uninhabitable and leading most of its population to be evacuated to the United Kingdom?

a. Aruba
b. Montserrat
c. Nevis
d. Anguilla

SOLUTIONS

1. A. Pharos of Alexandria. The pharos (or lighthouse) at Alexandria stood over 300 feet tall and was one of the tallest buildings in the world before a series of three earthquakes - in 956 CE, 1303, and 1323 - damaged it beyond repair. Eventually, it was pulled down, and much of its stonework used to construct other buildings in the city.
2. C. Vesuvius.
3. B. Lake Geneva. The collapse of an entire mountainside near the village of Tauredunum on Lake Geneva in 563 CE caused the waters of the lake to swell and form a tsunami that traveled the entire length of the lake. Hundreds, if not thousands, of people living on the lakeside at the time were killed - when the lake was under Frankish control.
4. A. Tornado. What would now be classed as a category F4 tornado struck London on October 17, 1091, destroying the original timber London Bridge. There were, however, only two known fatalities.
5. B. England. The sinking of the White Ship in the English Channel killed more than 300 people, among them the heir to King Henry I's throne, William Adelin, and many more members of his immediate family.
6. B. The Netherlands. Parts of the Netherlands are so low-lying that the flood of 1287 permanently altered the country's geography, transforming many inland freshwater lakes - including the gigantic Zuiderzee - —into vast saltwater lagoons, connected to the coast. One of the worst floods in recorded history, the disaster is known as the St Lucia's Day Flood, as it took place on the night of the feast day of St. Lucia, December 13.
7. True! As well as being heard by people in Perth, Australia, the explosion was even reported by locals on the Indian Ocean island of Rodrigues, 3,000 miles west of Java.
8. A. Galveston. An immense storm surge driven inland by a Category 4 hurricane killed more than 6,000 people and caused more than $1¼ billions of damage.
9. B. Mining. An immense coaldust explosion killed more than 1,000 people.
10. D. Queenstown. The *Titanic* was constructed in Belfast, Northern Ireland. Its maiden voyage then led to it picking up passengers in Southampton, on the south coast of England, and Cherbourg, in

northern France, before arriving in Queenstown (now the Irish city of Cobh) and departing across the Atlantic from there.

11. D. Avalanche. On December 13, 1916, an avalanche struck several troops' barracks on Mount Marmolada in northern Italy, killing 270 soldiers.

12. D. Boston. A huge molasses tank in the city burst, sending a wave of molasses through the streets at an estimated 35 mph.

13. A. China. The immediate death toll from the immense floods that struck the Yangtze River basin in 1931 has been estimated at around a quarter of a million people. The number of people who then succumbed to starvation or cholera in the months after caused the death toll to rise to an estimated 4,000,000.

14. B. Chile.

15. D. 1974. The infamous 2011 super outbreak produced more than twice as many tornadoes as this, but the 1974 outbreak remains the most violent in US history, with 30 category F4 or F5 tornadoes confirmed in just 24 hours from April 3–4.

16. A. China.

17. C. India. A leak of highly toxic methyl isocyanate gas killed at least 2,000 (but perhaps as many as 10,000 or more) people in the surrounding area.

18. B. Montserrat.

DID YOU KNOW?

As well as the famous molasses flood of 1919, London suffered a beer flood in 1814!

21.
BRITISH KINGS & QUEENS

From the Battle of Hastings through to the coronation of King Charles III in 2023, the British - and before then, English - line of kings and queens is one of the longest-lasting lines of succession in the world. More than 40 individuals have held the throne in England and Great Britain, among them some of the world's longest and shortest reigning monarchs, and some of history's most famous and infamous characters. Test your knowledge of the British throne with these tricky questions...

1. What was the name of the king who William the Conqueror defeated to become King William I of England at the Battle of Hastings in 1066?

    a. Harold
    b. Edgar
    c. Edmund
    d. Alfred

2. William the Conqueror's successor, William II, died under somewhat questionable circumstances during a what?

    a. Sailing voyage
    b. Hunting trip
    c. Medical procedure
    d. Battle practice

3. When he died in 1199, which English king's heart was removed from his body and interred in a small casket in Rouen Cathedral in France?

    a. Stephen
    b. Henry II
    c. Richard I
    d. John

4. One of the earliest uses of the Tower of London was as a royal menagerie, which is why King Henry III kept his pet polar bear there. True or false?

5. For his brutal treatment of rebels north of the border, which medieval king became known as the Hammer of the Scots?

    a. Edward I
    b. Edward II
    c. John

d. Henry IV

6. In 1313, King Edward II made it illegal for what to be worn in the English Parliament?

    a. Hats
    b. Gloves
    c. Armor
    d. False limbs

7. Amassing just over nine years in power, who was the shortest reigning of England's eight King Henrys?

    a. Henry I
    b. Henry IV
    c. Henry V
    d. Henry VIII

8. Edward IV rose to the throne in 1461, after securing victory at the bloodiest battle ever waged on English soil. Where was it fought?

    a. Lincoln
    b. Towton
    c. Portsmouth
    d. Carlisle

9. Which English king is rumored to have had a hunched back?

    a. Richard III
    b. John
    c. William II
    d. Henry VI

10. The Babington Plot of 1586 was a plan to assassinate which Tudor monarch?

    a. Henry VII
    b. Henry VIII
    c. Mary I
    d. Elizabeth I

11. Who became king when the monarch was restored in England in 1660?

    a. James I

b. Charles I

c. Charles II

d. William III

12. William III remains the only king in British history to have ruled jointly with his wife. Who was she?

    a. Anne

    b. Elizabeth I

    c. Mary II

    d. Queen Charlotte

13. Which English queen became pregnant 18 times during her reign yet never produced an heir?

    a. Elizabeth I

    b. Anne

    c. Mary I

    d. Mary II

14. True or false: The last time an English king led his own troops into battle was in 1555.

15. Before Elizabeth II, Queen Victoria was England's longest-reigning monarch. How long did she reign for?

    a. 43 years

    b. 53 years

    c. 63 years

    d. 73 years

16. Two names have been used by eight different English monarchs throughout history. One of them is Henry - what is the other?

    a. George

    b. Edward

    c. William

    d. Charles

17. Because of the abdication crisis, Edward, Duke of Windsor was the last British monarch not to…what?

    a. Live in Buckingham Palace

    b. Serve in the army

    c. Visit India

d. Be crowned

18. How many children did Queen Elizabeth II have?

   a. One
   b. Two
   c. Three
   d. Four

SOLUTIONS

1. A. Harold. William's predecessor was the Anglo-Saxon King Harold Godwinson, Harold II.
2. B. Hunting trip. William died while hunting within the New Forest in 1100. According to one account, the king was accidentally shot in the chest by a nobleman named Walter Tirel, who was aiming at a stag. (Tirel allegedly abandoned the dying king and immediately fled to France!)
3. C. Richard I. Richard the Lionheart died in France, and while his heart was kept in Rouen (and rediscovered in the 19th century), the rest of his body was buried in Fontevraud Abbey, near Tours.
4. True! Henry was gifted a polar bear by the Norwegian king Haakon IV in 1252. He kept it in the Tower of London, from where it was taken down to the River Thames each day to swim and catch fish.
5. A. Edward I.
6. C. Armor. The act remains in force in the British parliament to this day.
7. C. Henry V. He died in France in 1422, aged just 36.
8. B. Towton. More than 50,000 troops are thought to have been involved in the Battle of Towton in March 1461, more than half of whom were killed in the fighting or by the brutal conditions on the day (the battle was waged during a blinding snowstorm on the North Yorkshire Moors).
9. A. Richard III.
10. D. Elizabeth I. The aim of the plot was to reinstate a Catholic monarch - namely Elizabeth's cousin Mary, Queen of Scots - on the English throne. The plot failed and Mary was executed the following year.
11. C. Charles II.
12. C. Mary II. William outlived his wife by eight years after her death in 1694 and ruled alone as king until 1702.
13. B. Anne. Queen Anne was riddled with ill health, and as she never produced a surviving child, the House of Stuart died with her in 1714. She was succeeded by her second cousin, George I.
14. False. Actually, it was more recent than that: George II fought at the Battle of Dettingen in 1743.
15. C. 63 years. From 1837 until her death in 1901.

16. B. Edward. As of the 2020s, there have been six Georges, eight Edwards, four Williams, and three Charles.
17. D. Be crowned. The Duke held the throne as King Edward VIII for just 326 days. Although his coronation had been due to take place on May 12, 1937, he abdicated to marry Wallis Simpson on December 11, 1936, and so was never officially crowned.
18. D. Four. Charles, Anne, Andrew, and Edward.

DID YOU KNOW?

The British Crown owns around half of the British shoreline.

22.
THE INDUSTRIAL
REVOLUTION

Beginning in England in the mid-18th century, the Industrial Revolution was a period of great scientific, economic, and technological progress. Instigated by the invention and development of several new timesaving items of machinery and industrial apparatus, the Revolution proceeded quickly, spreading from Great Britain into continental Europe, and from there around the world.

And as these new technologies continued to be honed and improved, the whole world began to step into a new era of mass production and technological advancement. Can you match your wits with the great thinkers of this period of history?

1. One of the very first crucial advances of the Industrial era was the invention of the spinning jenny, which was patented by the English inventor James Hargreaves in 1770. But what industry did it revolutionize?

   a. Pottery
   b. Textiles
   c. Farming
   d. Construction

2. Which Scottish inventor patented his much-improved design for a steam engine in 1769?

   a. James Watt
   b. Michael Faraday
   c. Samuel Crompton
   d. James Prescott Joule

3. True or false: One of the earliest purposes of the first steam engines in the Industrial Revolution was not to drive manufacturing machinery, but water pumps.

4. Which pioneer of the Industrial Age is known for being the first person to use steam engines in a factory setting, using a gigantic one to power ranks of textile-making machines?

   a. Robert Fulton
   b. Richard Trevithick
   c. Joseph Swan
   d. Richard Arkwright

5. In 1793, English-born businessman Samuel Slater established the first successful industrial cotton mill in the United States - in what state?

   a. Delaware
   b. Rhode Island
   c. Florida
   d. Virginia

6. And likewise in 1793, Eli Whitney invented the cotton gin - in which US state?

   a. Alabama
   b. Kentucky
   c. Georgia
   d. Vermont

7. In 1803, England's newly industrialized textile industry made cotton and cotton products the country's biggest exported commodity- overtaking the production of what?

   a. Clay
   b. Coal
   c. Wood
   d. Peat

8. In the 1810s, a movement against industrial progress emerged that saw protesters attack factories and machinery due to fears their jobs would be replaced by machines. What name was given to these anti-progress protestors?

   a. Moabites
   b. Janeites
   c. Luddites
   d. Jacobites

9. With what item of mining apparatus is the English inventor Sir Humphrey Davy most closely associated?

   a. Rock-crushing mill
   b. Safety lamp
   c. Underground elevator
   d. Conveyor belt

10. English inventor Joseph Aspdin is credited with creating a new building material called Portland in 1824. What kind of material is it?

   a. Weather-treated timber
   b. Steel girder
   c. Cement
   d. Safety glass

11. The 19th-century American inventor Cyrus McCormick is a name associated with the development of what industry?

   a. Agriculture
   b. Clothing
   c. Communications
   d. Architecture

12. Which of these famous names patented a new design for an industrial sewing machine in America in 1846?

   a. Peter Cooper
   b. Matthias Baldwin
   c. Elisha Otis
   d. Elias Howe

13. Connecticut inventor Eli Terry is known for his many innovations in the production of what in the early 1800s?

   a. Ovens
   b. Snowplows
   c. Clocks
   d. Pianos

14. Which of these Industrial Era innovations was further refined and improved by New York inventor George Henry Corliss in the 1840s?

   a. Steam engine
   b. Cotton mill
   c. Mechanical typewriter
   d. Combine harvester

15. In 1859, New Yorker Edwin Drake opened the first productive oil well in the United States of America, in what state?

   a. California
   b. South Carolina

c. Maine

d. Pennsylvania

16. In the 1860s, work began on a long cross-country railroad connecting the east and west coasts of America. With workers beginning on both sides of the country and working inward, where did the two lines meet?

a. Utah

b. Colorado

c. Texas

d. Oklahoma

17. Thomas Edison's incandescent light bulb, introduced in 1879, used what unlikely material for its glowing filament?

a. Porcelain

b. Bamboo

c. Human hair

d. Cotton

18. An unexpected consequence of the Industrial Revolution in England was that many people fled cities, seeking to escape the noise and pollution of the newly industrialized world: from the mid-1700s to the turn of the 1900s, the rural population in England shifted from 15% to 85%. True or false?

SOLUTIONS

1. B. Textiles. The spinning jenny was a yarn spinner fitted with multiple spindles, allowing a textile worker to work multiple spools at the same time. Initially fitted with eight wooden spindles, as technology improved spinning jennies with more than 100 spindles became common in the Victorian textile industry.
2. A. James Watt. Watt's own design was based around one of the earliest steam engines, the so-called Newcomen atmospheric engine, which had been patented more than 50 years earlier in 1712.
3. True. Many of the first steam engines were used to siphon water out of flooded coal mines, so that the production of coal - the driving force of the Industrial Revolution - would not be interrupted.
4. D. Richard Arkwright. Arkwright is now credited by some as being the founder of the modern mass-production factory.
5. B. Rhode Island. Slater's mill was opened in Pawtucket.
6. C. Georgia.
7. C. Wood.
8. C. Luddites. Supposedly named after an English laborer named Ned Ludd who had destroyed a weaving machine in 1779, the term *luddite* is still used for a stubborn opponent to change or new technology today.
9. B. Safety lamp. The so-called Davy lamp - a kind of illuminated wick, designed to be safely used in potentially flammable atmospheres below ground - was patented in 1815.
10. C. Cement.
11. A. Agriculture. McCormick invented a mechanical reaper, for speeding up the harvesting process, in 1834.
12. D. Elias Howe.
13. C. Clocks.
14. A. Steam engine. The Corliss steam engine was patented in 1849.
15. D. Pennsylvania. The well was dug at Titusville, around 80 miles north of Pittsburgh.
16. A. Utah. The two lines came together at Promontory, Utah, just north of Salt Lake City.

17. B. Bamboo. Edison's original patent was for a system that used specially treated and carbonized bamboo as the filament in his lightbulb, which it was found could reliably give over 1,000 hours of illumination.
18. False. In fact, those figures should be reversed as people fled from the countryside to find work in the cities - it was therefore England's urban population that rose from 15% to 85% in the 150 years from the mid-18th to early 20th centuries!

DID YOU KNOW?

Thomas Edison proposed to his wife in Morse code.

23.
THE 1800S

It's easy to think of the 1800s as the Victorian Era, given that the reign of one of Britain's longest-ruling monarchs spanned six of the century's 19th decades. But elsewhere around the world, in countries where the rule of Queen Victoria did not have quite such an impact, the 19th century was another great period of change and upheaval. So how much do you know about this extraordinary 100 years?

1. After a tie in the Electoral College, who did the House of Representatives name as US president in 1801?

   a. Thomas Jefferson
   b. James Madison
   c. John Adams
   d. James Monroe

2. Who was excommunicated by the Pope in 1809?

   a. King George III
   b. Napoleon
   c. Emperor Alexander I of Russia
   d. Charles IV of Spain

3. Spencer Percival was murdered in 1812. He is the only holder of what office to be assassinated?

   a. Vice President of Canada
   b. Speaker of the House of Representatives
   c. Prime Minister of Great Britain
   d. Mayor of New York

4. True or false: Demonstrated in 1813, William Hedley's Puffing Billy was one of the world's first paddle steamers.

5. In what year of the 1810s was Napoleon defeated at the Battle of Waterloo?

   a. 1811
   b. 1812
   c. 1815
   d. 1818

6. Which of these books was published earliest?

   a. *Wuthering Heights*

b. *Frankenstein*

c. *Pride and Prejudice*

d. *Oliver Twist*

7. Which country's Maratha Empire dissolved in 1820?

   a. China

   b. Russia

   c. Egypt

   d. India

8. Which European country broke away from the Ottoman Empire and declared its independence in 1821?

   a. Greece

   b. Italy

   c. Hungary

   d. Poland

9. In what decade of the 19th century did Ireland endure a famine?

   a. 1820s

   b. 1840s

   c. 1860s

   d. 1880s

10. Which country had a July Revolution in 1830?

    a. France

    b. United States

    c. China

    d. Egypt

11. Which US state briefly declared its independence in 1835?

    a. California

    b. New York

    c. Texas

    d. Florida

12. Which superpower was defeated in Europe's Crimean War in the 1850s?

    a. Ottoman Empire

    b. Egypt

c. India

d. Russia

13. What did Alfred Nobel, namesake of the Nobel Prizes, invent in 1867?

    a. Solar engine
    b. Dynamite
    c. Stainless steel
    d. Reinforced concrete

14. Which of these great engineering projects was completed in 1869?

    a. Panama Canal
    b. Aswan Dam
    c. Suez Canal
    d. Golden Gate Bridge

15. America endured one of the world's first national labor strikes in 1877, when workers in what industry ceased working on July 14?

    a. Textiles
    b. Brewing
    c. Railroads
    d. Newspapers

16. How many days after he was shot on Saturday, July 2, 1881, did President Garfield finally succumb to his injuries?

    a. 19
    b. 39
    c. 59
    d. 79

17. True or false: Coca-Cola was first developed way back in 1886.

18. Which country became the first in the world to give women the vote in 1893?

    a. Hungary
    b. Iceland
    c. New Zealand
    d. Monaco

SOLUTIONS

1. A. Thomas Jefferson.
2. B. Napoleon. The French army invaded the Papal States in 1809 and Napoleon installed his son as the King of Rome. As a result, he was excommunicated by Pope Pius VII.
3. C. Prime Minister of Great Britain. Percival was shot dead in the lobby of the House of Commons by a merchant from Liverpool, John Bellingham, who was enraged with his government's policies.
4. False. It was an early steam locomotive.
5. C. 1815.
6. C. *Pride and Prejudice*. Jane Austen's classic novel debuted in 1813. Mary Shelley published *Frankenstein* in 1818; Charles Dickens published *Oliver Twist* in 1837; and Emily Brontë's *Wuthering Heights* followed in 1847.
7. D. India.
8. A. Greece.
9. B. 1840s.
10. A. France.
11. C. Texas. The so-called Texas Revolution lasted from October 2, 1835, to April 21, 1836.
12. D. Russia.
13. B. Dynamite.
14. C. Suez Canal. The canal connected the Mediterranean Sea to the Red Sea and the wider Indian Ocean, shortening the sea journey from Europe to the Far East by several months.
15. C. Railroads. The so-called Great Railroad Strike of 1877 lasted for 52 days, with workers not returning to work until September 4.
16. D. 79. The shooting occurred just four months into Garfield's presidency; he died on September 19.
17. True.
18. C. New Zealand. A handful of smaller territories and dependencies - including the Pitcairn Islands (1838), Hawaii (1840), and what was at the time the Duchy of Tuscany (1848) - had already enacted forms of universal suffrage, but New Zealand was the world's first independent nation to follow suit.

DID YOU KNOW?

Although he is known for his short stature, it has been estimated Napoleon Bonaparte was around five feet seven inches tall - which was above average for a French man in the 19th century!

24.
US PRESIDENTS

The 40 or so holders of the US Presidency have included some extraordinarily varied characters - from a former lifeguard turned actor (Ronald Reagan) to a former hangman (Grover Cleveland). But what else do you know about the holders of the highest office in the land? Take this quiz to test your knowledge of the US Presidents of the past!

1. What was the name of the second President John Adams' wife?

   a. Annabel
   b. Abigail
   c. Adrienne
   d. Amity

2. Who was re-elected in the US election of 1820, in which he had no major opponent?

   a. George Washington
   b. James Monroe
   c. John Quincy Adams
   d. James K Polk

3. True or false: In 1806, future president Andrew Jackson shot and killed a man in a duel.

4. Who is credited with being the first US president who was born an American?

   a. Martin van Buren
   b. John Tyler
   c. Zachary Taylor
   d. Millard Fillmore

5. William Henry Harrison was famously the shortest-serving president in history. How long did he last?

   a. 12 days
   b. 32 days
   c. 52 days
   d. 72 days

6. Which early president's nickname was Old Rough and Ready?

   a. Franklin Pierce
   b. Zachary Taylor

c. John Tyler

d. James Buchanan

7. Franklin Pierce is the only US president to have hailed from which state?

    a. New Hampshire
    b. New York
    c. New Jersey
    d. New Mexico

8. Hannibal Hamlin was which 19th-century president's first vice president?

    a. Andrew Johnson
    b. James K Polk
    c. Andrew Jackson
    d. Abraham Lincoln

9. Which future US president - at the time a major figure in the Civil War - had been invited to attend the theater with President Lincoln the night that he was shot in 1845?

    a. Ulysses S Grant
    b. James A Garfield
    c. Rutherford B Hayes
    d. Grover Cleveland

10. Who was President James A Garfield's vice president, who assumed the presidency on his death in 1881?

    a. Grover Cleveland
    b. James Buchanan
    c. Millard Fillmore
    d. Chester A Arthur

11. Grover Cleveland is famously the only president in history to serve two non-consecutive terms. Numerically, which positions did he hold?

    a. 18 and 20
    b. 22 and 24
    c. 27 and 29
    d. 28 and 30

12. Who, when he took office in 1901, was the youngest person ever elected president at the age of 42?

    a. Grover Cleveland
    b. Benjamin Harrison
    c. William McKinley
    d. Theodore Roosevelt

13. Which of America's assassinated presidents was once portrayed on the $500 bill?

    a. Abraham Lincoln
    b. James A Garfield
    c. William McKinley
    d. John F Kennedy

14. In 1910, who became the first sitting president to throw the opening ceremonial pitch at a Major League Baseball game?

    a. Woodrow Wilson
    b. Warren G Harding
    c. Theodore Roosevelt
    d. William Howard Taft

15. Which 20th-century president had served just two years as governor of New Jersey - his only other experience in public office - before being elected president?

    a. John F Kennedy
    b. Herbert Hoover
    c. Calvin Coolidge
    d. Woodrow Wilson

16. Born in Oregon in 1874, who was the first president from west of the Mississippi?

    a. Herbert Hoover
    b. John F Kennedy
    c. Warren G Harding
    d. Harry S Truman

17. Which serving US president suffered a heart attack while visiting Denver in 1955, was later given a clean bill of health by his doctors, and won a second term the following year?

a. Harry S Truman
b. Lyndon B Johnson
c. Calvin Coolidge
d. Dwight D Eisenhower

18. What was Gerald Ford's middle name?

a. Rudolph
b. Randolph
c. Richard
d. Robin

SOLUTIONS

1. B. Abigail. The pair were remarkably close and exchanged more than 1,000 letters during their long relationship.
2. B. James Monroe. As these were the early days of the US presidency, this was the third time a president had run for re-election essentially unopposed.
3. True. The man had accused Jackson of cheating on a bet and then insulted his wife, leading to the pair holding a duel on May 30, 1806.
4. A. Martin van Buren. Van Buren was born in Kinderhook, New York. Ironically, as well as being the first American-born president, most of the residents in Van Buren's home neighborhood were of Dutch descent and spoke Dutch as their first language - which makes Van Buren also the only president to have spoken English as his second language.
5. B. 32 days. Harrison died of pneumonia just over four weeks after his inauguration as president in 1841.
6. B. Zachary Taylor.
7. A. New Hampshire. Pierce was born in Hillsborough, New Hampshire, on November 23, 1804.
8. D. Abraham Lincoln. In Lincoln's second term, beginning with the 1864 election, Hamlin was replaced as vice-presidential nominee by Andrew Johnson - who in turn replaced Lincoln as president after his assassination the following year.
9. A. Ulysses S Grant. Grant and his wife were forced to turn down the invite as they had already made plans to travel to New Jersey to visit family.
10. D. Chester A Arthur.
11. B. 22 and 24. Cleveland served from 1885–89, then again from 1893–97. In between, he lost to Benjamin Harrison in 1888 (despite winning the popular vote) and then returned to defeat his old rival in the 1892 election.
12. D. Theodore Roosevelt.
13. C. William McKinley. McKinley's note was discontinued in 1969.
14. D. William Howard Taft.
15. D. Woodrow Wilson.
16. A. Herbert Hoover

17. D. Dwight D Eisenhower
18. A. Rudolph.

DID YOU KNOW?

The S in Harry S Truman's name didn't stand for anything. It was meant as a tribute to both of Truman's grandfathers, both of whom had middle names starting with S.

25.
THE CHANGING WORLD

In the 19th and 20th centuries, the political and geographical landscape of the world changed like never before. Nations and empires rose and fell, broke apart, renamed and rebuilt themselves, shifted their borders, and constructed new capitals. How much of this changing world do you recall from the history books?

1. What city became the capital of China in 1949?

    a. Shanghai
    b. Xi'an
    c. Beijing
    d. Yangzhou

2. The layout of which newly founded global capital city was open to an international design competition in 1911?

    a. Canberra, Australia
    b. New Delhi, India
    c. Islamabad, Pakistan
    d. Pretoria, South Africa

3. The Spanish colony of Gran Colombia gained independence in 1811. It eventually split into two neighboring nations - Colombia and...where?

    a. Panama
    b. Brazil
    c. Ecuador
    d. Venezuela

4. Belgium gained its independence from which European country in 1831?

    a. Germany
    b. Norway
    c. France
    d. The Netherlands

5. What country was partitioned in 1992, partly because of the Velvet Revolution of three years earlier?

    a. Sudan
    b. Czechoslovakia
    c. Finland

d.   India

6. Which Central American nation changed its capital from Cartago to San José in 1823?

    a.   Nicaragua
    b.   El Salvador
    c.   Honduras
    d.   Costa Riva

7. True or false: Tokyo hasn't always been called Tokyo and only gained its current name in 1868.

8. By what name was the Yugoslav city of Podgorica - now in Montenegro - known until 1992?

    a.   Titograd
    b.   Leningrad
    c.   Ivangrad
    d.   Kaliningrad

9. In what year did Australia become a self-governing Dominion in the British Empire, and thus its own nation of the Commonwealth of Australia?

    a.   1800
    b.   1850
    c.   1901
    d.   1950

10. What region of Asia was annexed by the People's Republic of China in 1951?

    a.   Kashmir
    b.   Outer Mongolia
    c.   Kamchatka
    d.   Tibet

11. Which of these countries declared its independence from Russia in 1917?

    a.   Finland
    b.   Turkey
    c.   Pakistan

    d.   Kazakhstan

12. Iceland gained independence from which country in 1918?

    a.   United Kingdom
    b.   United States
    c.   Denmark
    d.   Russia

13. Which Caribbean island moved its capital from Spanish Town to Kingston in 1872?

    a.   Cuba
    b.   Jamaica
    c.   Barbados
    d.   Aruba

14. What country broke away from China in 1921 and was recognized as an independent country by the United Nations 20 years later?

    a.   Macau
    b.   Laos
    c.   Cambodia
    d.   Mongolia

15. Which country adopted its current name, Myanmar, in 1989?

    a.   Burma
    b.   Taiwan
    c.   Hong Kong
    d.   Kampuchea

16. Which African country had been known as Bechuanaland until its independence from the United Kingdom in 1966?

    a.   Ghana
    b.   Liberia
    c.   Botswana
    d.   Benin

17. Which of these national changes of name happened most recently?

    a.   Siam became Thailand
    b.   Ceylon became Sri Lanka
    c.   Swaziland became Eswatini

d. Persia became Iran

18. Which African nation was formerly a British colony known as Rhodesia?

   a. Zimbabwe
   b. Libya
   c. Ethiopia
   d. Mozambique

SOLUTIONS

1. C. Beijing.
2. A. Canberra, Australia. The competition received 137 valid entries, of which a design by two US architects—Walter Burley Griffin and Marion Mahony Griffin—was chosen.
3. A. Panama.
4. D. The Netherlands
5. B. Czechoslovakia. The dissolution of Czechoslovakia formed the Czech Republic and Slovakia.
6. D. Costa Rica.
7. True. Before then, Tokyo was named Edo.
8. A. Titograd
9. C. 1901.
10. D. Tibet.
11. A. Finland.
12. C. Denmark. Iceland became a sovereign state after the signing of the Danish–Icelandic Act of Union on December 1, 1918.
13. B. Jamaica.
14. D. Mongolia.
15. A. Burma.
16. C. Botswana.
17. C. Swaziland became Eswatini. Sri Lanka adopted its current name in 1972, Siam became Thailand in 1939, and Iran was known as Persia until 1935. The name of Swaziland was officially changed to its local name, Eswatini, by the king as recently as 2018.
18. D. Zimbabwe.

DID YOU KNOW?

As well as changing its name from Edo, Tokyo replaced Kyoto as the capital of Japan in 1868. The change is thought to be the only time in history when one city whose name is an anagram of another has replaced it as capital!

26.
POLITICS & POLITICIANS

History is often shaped by the people in charge, of course, whether they be kings, queens, and emperors or elected leaders and heads of state. Our politics and politicians have ultimately had a vast impact on how our world has developed over the centuries, affecting everything from wars and revolutions to international diplomacy and industrial development. From presidents and prime ministers to dictators and political firebrands, this quiz is all about politicians and political figureheads.

1. Britain's first female prime minister, Margaret Thatcher, remained in power throughout every year of which decade?

   a. 1960s
   b. 1970s
   c. 1980s
   d. 1990s

2. Which famous political leader of the 20th century was imprisoned on Robben Island for 18 years before coming to power?

   a. Winston Churchill
   b. Nelson Mandela
   c. Mahatma Gandhi
   d. Joseph Stalin

3. Mrs. Sirimavo Bandaranaike became the world's first female prime minister when she was elected leader of which country in 1960?

   a. Myanmar
   b. Cambodia
   c. Israel
   d. Sri Lanka

4. In 1964, who succeeded Nikita Khrushchev as leader of the Soviet Union?

   a. Mikhail Gorbachev
   b. Joseph Stalin
   c. Leonid Brezhnev
   d. Yuri Andropov

5. True or false: Despite his connection to the United Kingdom, Winston Churchill was only half-British by birth - his mother was an American citizen.

6. Emilio Aguinaldo is a famous political leader in the independence movement of which island nation?

    a. Philippines
    b. New Zealand
    c. Cuba
    d. Bahamas

7. True or false: The title of Vice President of the United States was originally given to the candidate who came second in the electoral college, not a presidential candidate's running mate.

8. What was Mahatma Gandhi's job before he became a political figurehead and activist?

    a. Lawyer
    b. Teacher
    c. Journalist
    d. Actor

9. What is the present-day name of the country in which Nazi leader Adolf Hitler born in 1889?

    a. Germany
    b. Austria
    c. Belgium
    d. Switzerland

10. Which of these famous political names is an epithet, derived from the Russian word for steel?

    a. Rasputin
    b. Stalin
    c. Lenin
    d. Brezhnev

11. Clementine was the name of which famous wartime leader's wife?

    a. Woodrow Wilson
    b. Neville Chamberlain
    c. Winston Churchill
    d. Franklin D Roosevelt

12. Which Chinese politician is credited with establishing the People's Republic in 1949?

    a. Mao Zedong
    b. Yuan Shikai
    c. Chiang Kai-shek
    d. Lin Sen

13. Which president of France served during World War II and was eventually succeeded by Georges Pompidou in 1969?

    a. Vincent Auriol
    b. Philippe Pétain
    c. Albert Lebrun
    d. Charles de Gaulle

14. John A Macdonald was the first prime minister of what country?

    a. New Zealand
    b. Australia
    c. Canada
    d. South Africa

15. Who was the first Vice President of the United States to NOT go on to become president himself?

    a. Elbridge Gerry
    b. Aaron Burr
    c. Daniel D Tompkins
    d. John C Calhoun

16. The politician and activist Ali Jinnah was the political founder of which Asian nation?

    a. Bangladesh
    b. Burma
    c. Pakistan
    d. Mongolia

17. Who was the founder and first prime minister of Israel?

    a. Golda Meir
    b. David Ben-Gurion
    c. Yitzhak Rabin
    d. Moshe Sharett

18. Which long-serving Chancellor of Germany oversaw the end of the Cold War and the fall of the Berlin Wall?

    a. Willy Brandt
    b. Gerhard Schröder
    c. Ludwig Erhard
    d. Helmut Kohl

SOLUTIONS

1. C. 1980s. Thatcher came to power in 1979 and stepped down in 1990, meaning her 11-year prime ministership lasted the entire 1980s.
2. B. Nelson Mandela. Mandela was sentenced to 27 years in prison for his anti-apartheid political activism and served most of his term on Robben Island off the coast of Cape Town in South Africa. He was elected president in 1994, and he remained in power until 1999.
3. D. Sri Lanka. At the time, Sri Lanka was known as Ceylon.
4. C. Leonid Brezhnev. Brezhnev ruled for almost the next two decades, first as First Secretary and then General Secretary of the Communist Party, until his death in 1982.
5. True. Churchill's mother was Jennie Jerome, the Brooklyn-born daughter of a New York financier, who was a well-known socialite in the city.
6. A. Philippines.
7. True! When the office was first created in 1789, the president had no choice over his vice president. When a tie split the Electoral College in 1800, the Twelfth Amendment was added to the Constitution ahead of the 1804 election to create the current system.
8. A. Lawyer. Gandhi was called to the bar in 1891, at the age of 22.
9. B. Austria. Hitler was born in the town of Braunau am Inn, 40 miles north of Salzburg, close to the modern German border. At the time, it was in Austria-Hungary.
10. B. Stalin. Born into a family from Georgia, in the Caucasus Mountains, Stalin's name by birth was Ioseb Besarionis dze Jughashvili.
11. C. Winston Churchill.
12. A. Mao Zedong. Widely known around the globe as Chairman Mao, Mao Zedong remained in power until his death in 1976.
13. D. Charles de Gaulle.
14. C. Canada. In a political career spanning half a century, Macdonald served two terms as Canadian prime minister, first from 1867–73, and then again from 1878–91.
15. B. Aaron Burr. Burr was the United States' third vice president but was preceded in office by John Adams (who then went on to serve as president from 1797–1801) and Thomas Jefferson (president 1801–09).

Burr served under Jefferson during his first term, from 1801–05, but unlike his predecessors never assumed the office of president himself.

16. C. Pakistan.
17. B. David Ben-Gurion. Ben-Gurion served two terms as Israeli prime minister, 1948–53, and then again from 1955–63.
18. D. Helmut Kohl. Kohl served for more than 16 years, from 1982–98, becoming Germany's longest-serving head of state since Otto von Bismarck.

DID YOU KNOW?

Although best known as "The Iron Lady," in the UK Margaret Thatcher was also known as "The Milk Snatcher" because of her removal of free bottles of milk from English schools.

27.
CIVIL WAR AMERICA

Lasting from the spring of 1861 to the spring of 1865, the American Civil War was the culmination of many decades of rumbling concern about the future of the newly emerging United States. With the expansion or eventual eradication of slave states a notably hot topic since the nation's very earliest days, the outcome of the war set the US on a new and more progressive path as it headed toward the 20th century. Against the backdrop of the war, however, many other notable events took place - including many we'll touch on in this quiz dedicated to this most turbulent and controversial era in America's history.

1. Following Abraham Lincoln's victory in the 1860 election, 11 states seceded from the Union. Which was the first?

   a. Florida
   b. Alabama
   c. South Carolina
   d. Tennessee

2. In what Southern state capital were the Confederate States of America formerly established on February 4, 1861?

   a. Montgomery
   b. Nashville
   c. Richmond
   d. Raleigh

3. The first clash of the Civil War was the Confederate attack on Fort Sumner in April 1861 - in which city?

   a. Charleston
   b. Wilmington
   c. Blountville
   d. Charlotte

4. One of the earliest battles of the Civil War was the Battle of Bull Run. But what - and where - is Bull Run?

   a. A lake in Arkansas
   b. A hilltop in South Carolina
   c. A stream in Virginia
   d. A beach in Louisiana

5. The Battle of Hampton Roads, the first major naval battle of the Civil War, was also the first battle between ironclad warships in history. But what was the name of the Union warship that went up against the Confederate CSS *Virginia*?

    a. USS *Monitor*
    b. USS *Mahopac*
    c. USS *Ironsides*
    d. USS *Galena*

6. Which Confederate general was killed in fighting at the Battle of Shiloh - also known as the Battle of Pittsburg Landing - in April 1862?

    a. Thomas Green
    b. Albert Sidney Johnston
    c. John T Hughes
    d. Jeffrey E Forrest

7. True or false: Allan Pinkerton - the founder of the famous Pinkerton Detective Agency - put his sleuthing skills to good use during the Civil War, by directing espionage schemes for the Union and sending his agents undercover in the Confederate Army.

8. Who was the Union leader of the troops at the disastrous Battle of Chancellorsville in the spring of 1863?

    a. Joseph Hooker
    b. Robert Anderson
    c. DD Porter
    d. John Pope

9. On what date in 1863 was the Emancipation Proclamation issued?

    a. January 1
    b. February 14
    c. July 4
    d. December 25

10. Who was the Union commander at the Battle of Gettysburg?

    a. Adolph von Steinwehr
    b. John F Reynolds
    c. Joshua Lawrence Chamberlain
    d. George Meade

11. What city in western Mississippi was famously besieged by Union forces for several weeks until July 4, 1863, after which the Union took complete control of the Mississippi River?

    a. Gulfport
    b. Tupelo
    c. McComb
    d. Vicksburg

12. At what Civil War battle did Pickett's Charge take place?

    a. Gettysburg
    b. New Orleans
    c. Five Forks
    d. Chattanooga

13. In what state was General Grant's brutal Overland Campaign - which led to the deaths of more than 10,000 troops - waged in the summer of 1863?

    a. Virginia
    b. South Carolina
    c. Kentucky
    d. Ohio

14. In the winter of 1864, which Union general led an infamous March to the Sea, destroying and burning almost everything in his and his troops' path across Georgia?

    a. Ambrose Burnside
    b. Andrew Foote
    c. William Sherman
    d. Joseph Hooker

15. Where did Robert E Lee surrender to the forces of Ulysses S Grant on April 9, 1865?

    a. Appomattox
    b. Raleigh
    c. Atlanta
    d. Gatlinburg

16. True or false: Two years before he was assassinated in Ford's Theater in 1865, Abraham Lincoln survived an earlier attempt on his life as he was riding home one evening in 1863.

17. Who famously referred to Ulysses S Grant as a "butcher" for enduring such heavy losses during the war?

    a. Harriet Tubman
    b. William Sherman
    c. Mary Lincoln
    d. Andrew Jackson

18. Which of these states and territories officially maintained a neutral stance during the Civil War?

    a. Rhode Island
    b. Hawaii
    c. Guam
    d. Puerto Rico

SOLUTIONS

1. C. South Carolina. South Carolina became the first state to secede from the federal Union on December 20, 1860. Six more - Mississippi, Florida, Alabama, Georgia, Louisiana, and Texas - quickly followed suit. A final four - Virginia, Arkansas, Tennessee, and North Carolina - eventually joined them to form the Confederate States of America.
2. A. Montgomery.
3. A. Charleston.
4. C. A stream in Virginia. Fought on July 21, 1861, the Battle of Bull Run was also known as the First Battle of Manassas.
5. A. USS *Monitor*.
6. B. Albert Sidney Johnston. Johnston was shot in the knee on the afternoon of the first of two days of fighting at Shiloh on April 6 and died just minutes later. The bullet had torn an artery in his leg, and he died of blood loss on the battlefield.
7. True. Pinkerton's war efforts proved not entirely reliable, however, with one historian labeling the espionage data he and his men managed to accumulate "the poorest intelligence service any general ever had."
8. A. Joseph Hooker.
9. A. January 1.
10. D. George Meade. It was US Army Major General Meade - commander of the Army of the Potomac from 1863 to 1865 - whose troops faced those of the Confederate General Robert E Lee.
11. D. Vicksburg. The Union's victory at the Siege of Vicksburg proved a turning point in the war, as it split the Confederate forces into two halves.
12. A. Gettysburg
13. A. Virginia.
14. C. William Sherman. Sherman's march took just over a month, from November 15 to December 21, 1864.
15. A. Appomattox. Lee's surrender took place in Appomattox Court House in central Virginia.
16. True. While riding back to his summer retreat, Soldiers' Home, one evening in August 1863, an unknown assailant shot at Lincoln from the foot of a nearby hill, with the bullet knocking his hat from his head. He

reportedly asked the guards who came to his assistance to keep the event quiet for fear of worrying his wife.

17. C. Mary Lincoln. Mary was referring specifically to the enormous loss of life Grant's controversial Overland Campaign had endured in the spring of 1864.

18. B. Hawaii. Both Puerto Rico and Guam were not American territories in the Civil War era, while Rhode Island remained loyal to the Union alongside all the other states of New England. At the time of the war, Hawaii was still the Kingdom of Hawaii and had close military ties with both the UK and the United States. Although its leader, King Kamehameha IV, officially declared the islands' neutrality on August 26, 1861, many native Hawaiians both at home and on the American mainland enlisted in the army and are recorded among both Union and Confederate troops.

DID YOU KNOW?

The Battle of Dranesville, fought in Fairfax County, Virginia, is said to be the shortest battle of the US Civil War. It lasted just three hours, on the afternoon of December 20, 1861.

28.
AFRICAN HISTORY

Given that all of humanity itself can trace its history back to central Africa, perhaps the history of Africa is the longest and most intricate of all the world's regions. We're not going to go quite that far back in time with these questions, but we're still going to test your knowledge of more than 5,000 years of history...

1. Which of these ancient figures ruled Egypt earliest?

    a. Ramses the Great
    b. Akhenaten
    c. Tutankhamun
    d. Cleopatra

2. What was the name of the grand Bronze Age kingdom that developed south of Ancient Egypt, and with which it shared many cultural and diplomatic ties in the first millennium BCE?

    a. Namibia
    b. Kush
    c. Assyria
    d. Umayyad

3. Mansa Musa, the king of the Mali Empire in the early 14th century, is popularly said to have been...what?

    a. Related to Tutankhamun
    b. Father to 300 children
    c. The richest person ever to have lived
    d. Medieval Africa's first recorded playwright

4. Based around five Ancient Greek colonies founded there in the 7th century BCE, in what African nation is the ancient region of Cyrenaica?

    a. Ghana
    b. Morocco
    c. Libya
    d. Somalia

5. True or false: Four of the Seven Wonders of the Ancient World were in Africa.

6. Who conquered Egypt in 331 BCE?

    a. Julius Caesar

b. Alexander the Great

c. Darius of Persia

d. Kublai Khan

7. Founded by the Phoenicians in the first millennium BCE, in which modern-day country did the city of Carthage once stand?

a. Tunisia

b. Egypt

c. Sudan

d. Senegal

8. Who was Carthage's opponent in the three Punic Wars fought between 264 and 146 BCE?

a. Greece

b. Rome

c. Arabia

d. Persia

9. The African kingdom of Abyssinia was founded in the 1200s. Which modern-day country does it roughly correspond to?

a. Nigeria

b. Ethiopia

c. Mozambique

d. Algeria

10. In what century did the Portuguese explorer Vasco da Gama sail four ships from Lisbon down around the southern tip of Africa and on to India, linking Europe and Asia by sea for the first time?

a. 12th century

b. 13th century

c. 14th century

d. 15th century

11. The Kikuyu people developed as a distinct culture in the 17th century - in which present-day African nation?

a. Angola

b. Namibia

c. Nigeria

d. Kenya

12. Which European country established its Cape Colony, or Kaapkolonie, on the south coast of Africa in 1652?

    a. The Netherlands
    b. France
    c. Italy
    d. England

13. Which European leader fought the Battle of the Pyramids in 1798?

    a. Duke of Wellington
    b. Napoleon Bonaparte
    c. Admiral Nelson
    d. Frederick the Great of Prussia

14. Which African capital city was established by British anti-slave campaigners in 1816, as a way of controlling and disrupting the slave trade on Africa's west coast?

    a. Conakry, Guinea
    b. Accra, Ghana
    c. Dakar, Senegal
    d. Banjul, Gambia

15. Which African country declared its independence in 1847, making it Africa's first and oldest surviving republic?

    a. Benin
    b. Liberia
    c. The Gambia
    d. Cameroon

16. In which African nation was the Orange Free State, which waged a series of wars against British rule in the late 19th and early 20th centuries?

    a. Egypt
    b. Kenya
    c. Ghana
    d. South Africa

17. From which country did Libya gain its independence in 1951?

a. Italy
b. United States
c. Spain
d. Denmark

18. In what decade did Idi Amin lead a violent coup in Uganda, to oust the president, Milton Obote, from power?

a. 1940s
b. 1950s
c. 1960s
d. 1970s

SOLUTIONS

1. B. Akhenaten. Pharaoh Akhenaten ruled 1352–1336 BCE; King Tutankhamun is popularly claimed to have been one of his sons and ruled in 1332–1324 BCE; Ramses the Great (aka Ramesses II) ruled for much of the following century, 1279–1213 BCE; and Queen Cleopatra was one of Egypt's final rulers, 52–30 BCE.
2. B. Kush.
3. C. The richest person ever to have lived. Mansa Musa's empire lay both on the edge of significant gold reserves and halfway along the main salt trading routes through the Sahara Desert. By producing gold and taxing trade through his kingdom, he is said to have amassed more wealth than any other individual in recorded history.
4. C. Libya. The Greeks established the city of Cyrene on the Mediterranean coast of Libya in 631 BCE, and eventually developed four other important colonies - known collectively as the Pentapolis of Cyrenaica - in the years that followed.
5. False. Actually, there were just two, both in Egypt: the Great Pyramid of Giza, and the Pharos of Alexandria.
6. B. Alexander the Great.
7. A. Tunisia
8. B. Rome.
9. B. Ethiopia.
10. D. 15th century. Da Gama's first voyage lasted from 1497–99.
11. D. Kenya.
12. A. The Netherlands. Great Britain established its own Cape Colony - later known as the Cape of Good Hope - in the 19th century, but the Netherlands' was the region's first. Both later proved imperative in the foundation of South Africa.
13. B. Napoleon Bonaparte.
14. D. Banjul, Gambia. The city of Banjul began life as an English base called Bathurst, named after Henry, the 3rd Earl Bathurst, who was British Secretary of State for War and the Colonies at the time.
15. B. Liberia. Liberia emerged from American colonies, and having declared its independence, was officially recognized as an independent state by the USA in 1862. Its capital, Monrovia, is named after US President James Monroe.

16. D. South Africa. The Orange Free State was one of the belligerents in the Boer Wars that were fought between the United Kingdom and South Africa's Boer republics from 1880–81 and 1899–1902.
17. A. Italy.
18. D. 1970s. Amin came to power in 1971.

DID YOU KNOW?

Africa was home to the world's tallest building for over 3,800 years. At 481 feet, the Great Pyramid of Giza was the tallest structure in the world until the construction of England's Lincoln Cathedral in 1311!

29.
VICTORIAN &
EDWARDIAN BRITAIN

The Victorian Era commenced in England with the accession of Queen Victoria to the throne in 1837. She remained Queen for the next 63 years, until her death at the age of 81 in 1901 - at which point her eldest son, Edward, rose to the British throne to become King Edward VII, and the turn-of-the-century Edwardian Era got underway. Victoria's longevity meant that Edward was already 60 years old when he came to the throne, and sadly he did not share his mother's long life.

He died of multiple causes - having suffered several heart attacks and an earlier smoking-related cancer - in 1910, and the short-lived Edwardian Era came to an end after just a decade. Together, however, the Victorian and Edwardian ages were to prove truly world-changing and epoch-defining periods of history. So, what do you remember about them?

1. How was Queen Victoria related to her predecessor on the British throne, William IV?

   a. Sister
   b. Daughter
   c. Niece
   d. Cousin

2. Introduced in Victorian Britain in 1840, the Penny Black was the world's first what?

   a. Taxicab
   b. Postage stamp
   c. Hair dye
   d. Wristwatch

3. In what year of Victoria's reign was slavery abolished across the entire British Empire?

   a. 1838
   b. 1858
   c. 1878
   d. 1898

4. Signed in 1846, the Treaty of Nanking ceded what colonial territory to Great Britain?

   a. Hong Kong
   b. Bermuda

c. Montserrat

d. Antarctica

5. The Bow Street Runners were withdrawn in 1839 after 90 years in operation. What were they?

   a. An early police force
   b. An early postal service
   c. An early taxi service
   d. An early suffragette movement

6. Who did Queen Victoria marry in 1840?

   a. Prince Henry
   b. Prince Edward
   c. Prince George
   d. Prince Albert

7. What was the name given to the vast international exhibition organized in Hyde Park in 1851?

   a. Grand Exposition
   b. Giant Show
   c. Global Fair
   d. Great Exhibition

8. London physician John Snow became the first person to recognize that what disease was transmitted by contaminated water in 1854?

   a. Malaria
   b. Cholera
   c. Polio
   d. Dysentery

9. Queen Victoria was the first reigning English monarch to live in what prominent royal residence?

   a. Buckingham Palace
   b. Sandringham
   c. Balmoral
   d. Windsor Castle

10. Which famous British newspaper was first published in 1855?

a. *The Times*
b. *The Telegraph*
c. *The Daily Mail*
d. *The Guardian*

11. True or false: Despite her long reign, Queen Victoria had just one child.

12. What London landmark was completed in 1859?

a. Nelson's Column
b. Marble Arch
c. Big Ben clock tower
d. The Mall

13. In 1876, Queen Victoria was granted what additional title?

a. Empress of India
b. Queen of Sheba
c. Prime Minister of Canada
d. Premier of Bermuda

14. What became compulsory in England and Wales in 1880?

a. Voting
b. Education
c. Military service
d. Jury service

15. How many times during Queen Victoria's reign did William Gladstone serve as her prime minister?

a. Two
b. Three
c. Four
d. Five

16. With which European power did Britain sign the Entente Cordiale agreement in 1904?

a. Ireland
b. Italy
c. Spain
d. France

17. In what year did Great Britain first host the Olympic Games, the first of the three times to date that the Games have been held there?

    a. 1896
    b. 1900
    c. 1904
    d. 1908

18. Who succeeded Edward VII as king in 1910?

    a. George V
    b. Edward VIII
    c. George VI
    d. Elizabeth II

SOLUTIONS

1. C. Niece. King William had no surviving legitimate children at the time of his death in 1837, meaning the throne passed to the only child of his brother, Prince Edward, Duke of Kent and Strathearn.
2. B. Postage stamp.
3. A. 1838. Britain's Slavery Abolition Act was passed in 1833, under Victoria's predecessor William IV, but it did not come into force until the second year of her reign. Slavery across the British Empire was officially ended on August 1, 1838.
4. A. Hong Kong. It remained a British-held territory until 1997.
5. A. An early police force. Based around Bow Street in central London, the Runners were essentially police law enforcement officers attached to the Bow Street Magistrates' Court in the City of Westminster. The introduction of the Police Act - and London's first formal police service - in 1839 brought the service to an end.
6. D. Prince Albert.
7. D. Great Exhibition. The Exhibition was partly the brainchild of Victoria's husband, Prince Albert.
8. B. Cholera. Snow noticed a cluster of cholera cases around a water pump in central London.
9. A. Buckingham Palace. Purchased a century earlier by George III in 1761, Buckingham Palace was originally used only as a royal consort's residence - first used by George's wife, Queen Charlotte - and was known as the Queen's House. It wasn't until 1837 that Buckingham Palace became the official London residence of the British monarch, with Queen Victoria to first ruling power to utilize it.
10. B. *The Telegraph*.
11. False. In fact, Victoria and Albert had nine children in total, who each married into so many other European royal houses that she later earned the nickname "The Grandmother of Europe."
12. C. Big Ben clock tower. The tower was renamed the Elizabeth Tower in 2012, to celebrate the Diamond Jubilee of Queen Elizabeth II.
13. A. Empress of India. In 1876, the British government passed a new act of parliament - The Royal Titles Act 1876 - granting Victoria and her successors the ability to hold the title Empress (or Emperor) of India.

14. B. Education. The Education Act of 1880 made primary education compulsory for all 5–10-year-olds.
15. C. Four.
16. D. France.
17. D. 1908. King Edward VII opened the Games on April 27.
18. A. George V.

DID YOU KNOW?

In Victorian England, fine sunny weather was known as "Queen's Weather," because Queen Victoria had such a reputation for having fair conditions on the days of her royal visits.

30.
THE WORLD WARS

The world has twice been thrown into global conflicts, first from 1914–18, and then again from 1939–45. Both wars commenced in Europe but eventually grew so large that more countries worldwide were involved in the wars than were not - especially given the breadth of Britain and Europe's empires at the time. Time to test your knowledge about these world-shaping conflicts.

1. World War I began after the assassination of Archduke Franz Ferdinand in 1914 in which European city?

   a. Geneva
   b. Utrecht
   c. Lodz
   d. Sarajevo

2. Which of these European superpowers was NOT neutral during World War I?

   a. Switzerland
   b. Norway
   c. Ireland
   d. Spain

3. Two days before they invaded Belgium, which smaller state did Germany invade first on August 2, 1914?

   a. Liechtenstein
   b. Andorra
   c. Luxembourg
   d. Monaco

4. The Schlieffen Plan was Germany's World War I strategy to invade what country, not by crossing its borders with Germany, but via their mutual neighbors?

   a. Poland
   b. Austria
   c. France
   d. Switzerland

5. True or false: The same day the United Kingdom declared war on Germany in 1914, the United States declared its neutrality.

6. Which nation suffered an ignominious defeat at the Battle of Tannenberg in the summer of 1914?

   a. Russia
   b. Ottoman Empire
   c. Great Britain
   d. Germany

7. Which of these Belgian cities played host to five major battles during World War I?

   a. Liège
   b. Bruges
   c. Ypres
   d. Leuven

8. In what country is the Gallipoli peninsula, the site of a major Allied campaign — chiefly fought by Australian and New Zealand troops - in 1915?

   a. Denmark
   b. Turkey
   c. Russia
   d. Italy

9. In what year did Adolf Hitler become Chancellor of Germany?

   a. 1919
   b. 1925
   c. 1933
   d. 1939

10. On what date in 1939 did Nazi Germany invade Poland?

   a. January 1
   b. May 1
   c. September 1
   d. December 1

11. What kind of German war vessels were all given code names beginning with the letter U during World War I and II?

   a. Battleships
   b. Submarines

c. Airplanes

d. Tanks

12. Having originally championed a policy of appeasement with Nazi Germany, which British wartime prime minister resigned in 1940 to make way for Winston Churchill?

    a. Stanley Baldwin

    b. HH Asquith

    c. David Lloyd George

    d. Neville Chamberlain

13. The 14th-century medieval cathedral in what British city was famously destroyed in a German air raid in November 1940?

    a. Edinburgh

    b. Newcastle

    c. Coventry

    d. Plymouth

14. Launched in 1941, Operation Barbarossa was Nazi Germany's plan to invade…where?

    a. Norway

    b. England

    c. Spain

    d. Russia

15. Which was the westernmost of the five D-Day landing beaches?

    a. Juno

    b. Utah

    c. Omaha

    d. Sword

16. What Italian island was invaded and claimed by the Allies in the summer of 1943, leading to the surrender of Mussolini's Italy on September 3?

    a. Sicily

    b. Sardinia

    c. Capri

    d. Ischia

17. In what year was the Battle of Midway fought in the Pacific Ocean?

    a. 1941
    b. 1942
    c. 1943
    d. 1944

18. In the aftermath of World War II, in what German city were the trials of several remaining representatives of Hitler's Nazi government held between November 1945 and October 1946?

    a. Dresden
    b. Berlin
    c. Hamburg
    d. Nuremberg

SOLUTIONS

1. D. Sarajevo.
2. C. Ireland. Ireland was still part of the United Kingdom in 1914, and so was officially one of the Allied Powers along with France and Russia.
3. C. Luxembourg.
4. C. France. Germany invaded Luxembourg and Belgium to gain access to France without crossing Germany's own French border.
5. True.
6. A. Russia. Germany's use of local railway lines and the Russians' failure to encrypt their communications led to a near-total disaster for the Russian 2nd Army - and the suicide of its commanding general, Alexander Samsonov.
7. C. Ypres. The First (1914) and Second (1915) Battles of Ypres are the best known of these five local battles but were followed by the Passchendaele campaign (also known as the Third Battle of Ypres) in 1917, and both the Battle of Lys (known as the Fourth Battle of Ypres) and Advance in Flanders (popularly called the Fifth Battle of Ypres) in 1918.
8. B. Turkey
9. C. 1933.
10. C. September 1.
11. B. Submarines. The German submarines were known as *Unterseebooten* - literally "under-sea boats." To the Allied forces, they became known as U-boats.
12. D. Neville Chamberlain.
13. C. Coventry.
14. D. Russia.
15. B. Utah. From west to east along the England Channel coast of France, the beaches were Utah, Omaha, Gold, Juno, and Sword.
16. A. Sicily.
17. B. 1942.
18. D. Nuremberg.

DID YOU KNOW?

It has been estimated that more than 4% of the French population at the time died in World War I.

31.
REVOLTS & REVOLUTIONS

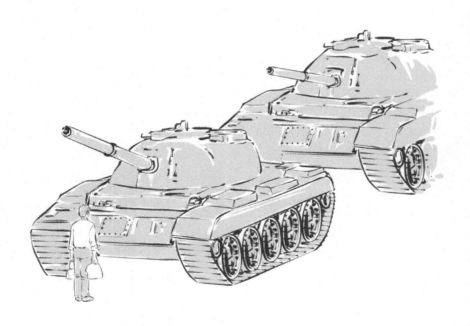

As well as wars and battles, the past is littered with tales of uprisings and protests, revolts, and revolutions, all of which - so long as they have proved successful enough! - Have gone on to change the course of their country's history. Covering more than three millennia of history, this quiz is dedicated to revolutions and rebellions from across the world. So, get ready with your best answers!

1. The first labor strike in recorded history took place in what ancient empire more than 3,000 years ago?

    a. Greece
    b. Rome
    c. Egypt
    d. Assyria

2. The so-called Rebellion of the Three Guards took place during the reign of the Zhou dynasty, in the late 11th century BCE, in what Asian country?

    a. Turkey
    b. Iran
    c. Afghanistan
    d. China

3. In 61 CE, the Celtic warrior queen Boudica and her forces protested against whose rule of ancient Britain?

    a. Vikings
    b. Romans
    c. Angles
    d. Normans

4. In an effort to end a series of rebellions objecting to his rule, which English king, in the winter of 1069, carried out a brutal series of scorched earth attacks on northern England known as the Harrying of the North?

    a. Ethelred
    b. Harold II
    c. William I
    d. Stephen

5. Which country's history includes rebellions known as the Red Eyebrow, the Yellow Turban, and the White Lotus?

    a. Russia
    b. Poland
    c. Syria
    d. China

6. In 1549, English Catholics rebelled against the court of King Edward VI in a short-lived uprising known as what?

    a. The Prayer Book Rebellion
    b. The Service Book Rebellion
    c. The Hymn Book Rebellion
    d. The Devotional Book Rebellion

7. In which country did a nobleman named Gustav Vasa launch a rebellion in 1521 that eventually led to the ousting of the king, Christian II, from the throne?

    a. Russia
    b. Sweden
    c. Ireland
    d. Hungary

8. America's so-called Whiskey Rebellion was a series of violent tax protests that occurred during whose presidency?

    a. George Washington
    b. Thomas Jefferson
    c. John Quincy Adams
    d. Abraham Lincoln

9. In Southampton County, Virginia, in 1831, Nat Turner led the bloodiest...what in American history?

    a. Naval mutiny
    b. Workers' protest
    c. Slave revolt
    d. Prison riot

10. In 1835, a republican revolt broke out in southern Brazil that came to be known by what peculiar name?

a. Ragamuffin Revolution
b. Urchin Revolution
c. Scoundrel Revolution
d. Rogue Revolution

11. Known as the Springtime of the People, in what year of the 19th century did a wave of people's revolutions take place across much of continental Europe?

    a. 1818
    b. 1848
    c. 1878
    d. 1898

12. Also known as Little Crow's War, in what US state did a famous Sioux Uprising take place in 1862?

    a. Missouri
    b. Montana
    c. Minnesota
    d. Mississippi

13. In what Asian country did the Satsuma Rebellion take place in 1877?

    a. Iran
    b. India
    c. Japan
    d. Korea

14. True or false: The turn-of-the-century Boxer Rebellion that broke out in China in 1899 was so named because many of the protesters openly carried boxes of ammunition around the streets.

15. In what year of the 1980s did the famous Tiananmen Square protests take place in China?

    a. 1981
    b. 1984
    c. 1986
    d. 1989

16. Following decades of war and rebellion as part of a 30-year struggle for national autonomy, which African nation finally declared itself independent from Ethiopia in 1991?

a. Cameroon
b. Eritrea
c. Somalia
d. Djibouti

17. What US city was rocked by violent riots in 1992?

a. Houston
b. Orlando
c. Los Angeles
d. Boston

18. In what country did a people's revolt lead to the ousting of President Hosni Mubarak in 2011, during one of the most tumultuous uprisings of the so-called Arab Spring?

a. Egypt
b. Tunisia
c. Algeria
d. Lebanon

SOLUTIONS

1. C. Egypt. Sometime during the reign of Ramses III in the 12th century BCE, a band of stoneworkers and laborers working in a village named Set-Ma'at in Egypt's famous Valley of the Kings downed tools in protest over delayed pay and supplies.

2. D. China. The Three Guards were three brothers of the founder king of the Zhou dynasty, Wu. After his death, another of Wu's brothers, Dan, took over the royal court as regent on behalf of Wu's son and heir, King Cheng, who was too young to lead on his own. The Three Guards were angered by what they saw as Dan's attempt to usurp their nephew and rose against the Zhou throne alongside a band of separatists still loyal to the previous Shang dynasty. The resulting conflict rumbled on for the next three years in northeast China, until the brothers were eventually defeated, and the Zhou throne passed safely on to Cheng when he came of age.

3. B. Romans. Although the larger force, Boudica's Iceni tribe and its allies were easily and decisively defeated by the invading Romans and the southern half of Britain remained a Roman territory as a result for the next 350 years.

4. C. William I. After the Norman Conquest, much of the north of England - which remained a stronghold of Celtic, Anglo-Saxon, and Viking culture - refused to accept his kingship and remained loyal to the previous English line of kings.

5. D. China.

6. A. The Prayer Book Rebellion. The rebels were objecting to the introduction of new theological guidance following the English Reformation, part of which banned Catholic processions and pilgrimages. The rebellion was quashed by the king's troops after only a matter of weeks, and more than two dozen of its leaders and protesters were executed.

7. B. Sweden.

8. A. George Washington.

9. C. Slave revolt. Turner's uprising against the enslavement in Southampton Country - known as the Southampton Insurrection - led to the deaths of more than 100 slaves and 50 local militiamen.

10. A. Ragamuffin Revolution.

11. B. 1848. The revolutions affected more than a dozen different countries, including France, Italy, Sweden, Germany, Denmark, Belgium, Spain, Ireland, and the United Kingdom. Some were more successful than others, however: the French Revolution of 1848 eventually led to the creation of the French Second Republic, but the Hungarian Revolution of 1848 failed in its goal to establish Hungary's independence from the Austrian Empire.
12. C. Minnesota.
13. C. Japan. As well as being the name of a kind of seedless orange widely grown there, Satsuma is a district in the Kagoshima prefecture of southern Japan.
14. False. In fact, the rebellion was so named because so many of those who took part were trained boxers and martial arts fighters.
15. D. 1989.
16. B. Eritrea.
17. C. Los Angeles.
18. A. Egypt.

DID YOU KNOW?

The famous individual in the Tiananmen Square photograph - standing in front of a tank - has never been identified.

32.
THE PACIFIC OCEAN

From the discovery of Australia and New Zealand by Western explorers through the Battle of Midway and the atomic bomb tests of World War II, the countries and islands of the Pacific Ocean have endured a long and colorful history. Let's see how much you know about it with these questions…

1. On what Pacific Ocean island were a series of gigantic stone monoliths, called *moai*, built by the local islanders between the 13th and 16th centuries?

    a. New Guinea
    b. Guam
    c. North Island, New Zealand
    d. Easter Island

2. Having crossed the Pacific Ocean from east to west, where was Ferdinand Magellan's first major landfall in 1521 while on his circumnavigation of the globe in the early 16th century?

    a. Guam
    b. Fiji
    c. Japan
    d. Java

3. Which explorer's first voyage to the Pacific Ocean in the 1640s ended in disaster when he arrived in New Zealand, and four of his crew were killed by Māori warriors?

    a. James Cook
    b. Abel Tasman
    c. António de Abreu
    d. Jorge Álvares

4. True or false: Daniel Defoe's 1719 story *Robinson Crusoe* is thought to have been inspired by the real-life discovery of a castaway on a remote Pacific island a decade earlier.

5. Although it became better known for its explorational successes, Captain Cook's first voyage to the Pacific Ocean was originally concerned with…what?

    a. Geology
    b. Meteorology

c. Astronomy

d. Medicine

6. Which Pacific Ocean island nation was first known to Westerners as the Friendly Islands, due to the hospitable reception afforded to Captain Cook when he arrived there for the first time in 1773?

a. Fiji

b. Tonga

c. Samoa

d. Hawaii

7. Many of which Pacific Ocean island's inhabitants are direct descendants of the mutineers of HMS *Bounty*, who arrived there in 1790?

a. Pitcairn Island

b. Christmas Island

c. Eastern Island

d. Clipperton Island

8. Which of these American-held territories in the Pacific Ocean was an independent sovereign nation for more than 80 years, from 1810–98?

a. Guam

b. American Samoa

c. Hawaii

d. Northern Mariana Islands

9. Where was Charles Darwin when he observed minute differences between local bird species, inspiring his groundbreaking theory of evolution in the 1830s?

a. Solomon Islands

b. Easter Island

c. Galapagos Islands

d. Hawaii

10. The Wilcox Rebellion of 1888 was an attempt to overthrow the king and queen of Hawaii while they were abroad at…what?

a. The Olympic Games

b. Queen Victoria's Golden Jubilee

c. The Paris World Fair

d. The opening of the Brooklyn Bridge

11. Which French artist famously spent most of his final years in Tahiti and the South Pacific in the 1890s?

a. Paul Gauguin

b. Claude Monet

c. Edouard Manet

d. Henri de Toulouse-Lautrec

12. In what year did aviator Amelia Earhart disappear over the Pacific Ocean during an attempt to become the first woman to complete a circumnavigational flight of the globe?

a. 1937

b. 1947

c. 1957

d. 1967

13. On what date in 1941 was the Japanese attack on Pearl Harbor, in Hawaii?

a. January 7

b. April 7

c. August 7

d. December 7

14. What decisive World War II naval battle was fought in the Pacific Ocean in June 1942?

a. Battle of the Coral Sea

b. Battle of Midway

c. Battle of Timor

d. Battle of the Bismarck Sea

15. Bikini Atoll, the coral island where more than 20 nuclear arms tests were carried out both during and after World War II, is part of what Pacific Ocean group?

a. Marshall Islands

b. Fiji

c. Tonga

d. Solomon Islands

16. In the famous photograph of the US military's flag raising on the island of Iwo Jima taken on February 23, 1945, how many soldiers are helping to raise the flag?

    a. Two
    b. Four
    c. Six
    d. Eight

17. Which Pacific Ocean island nation was suspended from the British Commonwealth of Nations in 2006 following a military coup d'état?

    a. Tuvalu
    b. Fiji
    c. Nauru
    d. Vanuatu

18. What New Zealand city was struck by an earthquake in 2011 that left 185 people dead?

    a. Dunedin
    b. Auckland
    c. Wellington
    d. Christchurch

SOLUTIONS

1. D. Easter Island.
2. A. Guam.
3. B. Abel Tasman. The sea between Australia and New Zealand is now named the Tasman Sea in his honor.
4. True! The castaway, Alexander Selkirk, lived alone on the second largest of Chile's Juan Fernández Islands - now named Robinson Crusoe Island in his honor - for five years, until his discovery in 1709.
5. C. Astronomy. Cook's voyage was originally chartered by Britain's naval admiralty in 1768 to observe the transit of Venus across the Sun from the South Seas, near Tahiti.
6. B. Tonga.
7. A. Pitcairn Island.
8. C. Hawaii. The Kingdom of Hawai'i was a sovereign nation from 1810 until 1893, when European and American settlers overthrew the native monarchy. The country remained independent for a further four years, until becoming a US territory in 1898, and finally a US state in 1959.
9. C. Galapagos Islands.
10. B. Queen Victoria's Golden Jubilee.
11. A. Paul Gauguin.
12. A. 1937. Earhart and her navigator Fred Noonan disappeared somewhere near the tiny and uninhabited Howland Island, about 1,700 nautical miles south of Honolulu.
13. D. December 7.
14. B. Battle of Midway. The battle proved such an impressive victory for the United States that it has since been ranked alongside the likes of the Battle of Trafalgar as one of the most important naval conflicts in history.
15. A. Marshall Islands. Ahead of the military tests, all 167 people who lived on Bikini Island had to be forcibly removed and have never been able to return.
16. C. Six. The men were later identified as Michael Strank, Harlon Block, Franklin Sousley, Ira Hayes, Rene Gagnon, and Harold Schultz. Three of them - Strank, Block and Sousley - all later went on to die on Iwo Jima, within a matter of weeks of the flag being raised and the photograph being taken.

17. B. Fiji.
18. D. Christchurch.

DID YOU KNOW?

It has been estimated that some of the smaller islands of the Pacific Ocean were first explored and inhabited by seafarers more than 5,000 years ago.

33.
SCANDALS & INTRIGUES

In more recent centuries and decades, the (often somewhat questionable!) behavior of our politicians and wider history-makers has colored our national and political past. Test your knowledge - and your memory - of these scandals, mysteries, and intrigues with this astonishing set of questions.

1. Which early US president dealt with the so-called XYZ Affair, which led to an undeclared "Quasi-War" between America and France?

   a. George Washington
   b. John Adams
   c. Thomas Jefferson
   d. James Monroe

2. Which US politician caused a scandal in the mid-1800s when he showed up drunk to his own vice-presidential inauguration?

   a. Schuyler Colfax
   b. Henry Wilson
   c. Adlai Stevenson
   d. Andrew Johnson

3. What was the name of Abraham Lincoln's Secretary of War, who resigned in 1862 due to corruption charges?

   a. John Bell
   b. William Learned Marcy
   c. Jefferson Davis
   d. Simon Cameron

4. During Andrew Jackson's presidency in the mid-19th century, merchant and politician Samuel Swartwout was found to have embezzled more than $1 million while serving as a customs collector in what east-coast city?

   a. Boston
   b. New York
   c. Miami
   d. Charleston

5. The Whiskey Ring was an infamous scandal that dogged which 19th-century US president?

a. Abraham Lincoln
b. Franklin Pierce
c. Grover Cleveland
d. Ulysses S Grant

6. In 1857, New York statesman Orsamus B Matteson was accused of defaming the House of Representatives by claiming most of its members were…what?

a. "Corrupt"
b. "Purchasable"
c. "Dishonest"
d. "Crooked"

7. Who was the first US president to face impeachment?

a. Andrew Johnson
b. Chester A Arthur
c. Franklin Pierce
d. Rutherford B Hayes

8. During World War I, a shortage of what wartime commodity led to the downfall of the British Prime Minister HH Asquith in 1915?

a. Shells
b. Barbed wire
c. Grenades
d. Bayonets

9. The Teapot Dome Scandal was the greatest scandal to occur in the United States during the presidency of Warren Harding. But what is - or was - the Teapot Dome?

a. Sports stadium
b. National monument
c. Oil field
d. Battleship

10. In the 1956 Suez Crisis, Britain and France joined which Middle Eastern nation's invasion of Egypt?

a. Jordan
b. Lebanon

c. Syria

d. Israel

11. In 1960, one of which US state's members of the House of Representatives was found drunk in the back of his car with an Argentine exotic dancer in the middle of Washington DC?

   a. Alabama

   b. Arizona

   c. Arkansas

   d. Alaska

12. On what Massachusetts island had US Senator Ted Kennedy attended a party on July 18, 1969, the night that he crashed his car off a bridge, leading to the death of his passenger, Mary Jo Kopechne?

   a. Chappaquiddick

   b. Martha's Vineyard

   c. Cuttyhunk

   d. Spectacle

13. The Profumo Affair was an infamous Cold War-era scandal that affected the government of what country in 1963?

   a. Italy

   b. Russia

   c. Canada

   d. United Kingdom

14. Which US president was dogged by the Iran-Contra Affair?

   a. Jimmy Carter

   b. Ronald Reagan

   c. George Bush

   d. Bill Clinton

15. Known for doggedly surviving a series of several scandalous revelations throughout his political career, Silvio Berlusconi was prime minister of what European country on three separate occasions in the 1990s and 2000s?

   a. Latvia

   b. Italy

c. Portugal

d. Greece

16. What Asian nation's populist president Chen Shui-bian became embroiled in years of scandals - including insider trading and forgery - following his reelection in 2004?

a. India

b. Yemen

c. Pakistan

d. Taiwan

17. What somewhat unlikely figure was involved in a failed attempt to oust the president of the African Republic of Equatorial Guinea in 2004?

a. Winston Churchill's granddaughter

b. Bill Clinton's nephew

c. Margaret Thatcher's son

d. Tony Blair's uncle

18. In what European country did the infamous Gürtel scandal come to light in 2009, in which it was discovered several members of the main national conservative party were implicated in a longstanding network of bribery, money laundering, and tax evasion?

a. Italy

b. Spain

c. Norway

d. Ireland

SOLUTIONS

1. B. John Adams. The affair took its name from three code letters used to disguise the names of three French diplomats involved in the scandal - Jean-Conrad Hottinguer (X), Pierre Bellamy (Y), and Lucien Hauteval (Z).
2. D. Andrew Johnson.
3. D. Simon Cameron.
4. B. New York.
5. D. Ulysses S Grant.
6. B. "Purchasable." Matteson himself was later found to have accepted money under questionable circumstances and resigned on February 27.
7. A. Andrew Johnson.
8. A. Shells. The so-called Shell Crisis of 1915 was caused by the shortsightedness of Asquith's government, which failed to keep up with the wartime demand for military shells on the war's Western Front.
9. C. Oil field. It later emerged that Harding's Secretary of the Interior, Albert Bacon Fall, had leased the Teapot Dome oil reserves - located on public land in Wyoming - to private oil companies without opening the process up to competitive bids.
10. D. Israel.
11. C. Arkansas. The scandal dogged Representative Wilbur Mills' political career for the rest of his life, yet he remained in office for another 17 years, until 1977.
12. A. Chappaquiddick.
13. D. United Kingdom. John Profumo was the Secretary of State for War in Prime Minister Harold Macmillan's government, who had become romantically involved with a 19-year-old woman, Christine Keeler.
14. B. Ronald Reagan.
15. B. Italy.
16. D. Taiwan.
17. C. Margaret Thatcher's son. For his role in apparently helping to finance the coup, Sir Mark Thatcher was later convicted and fined in South Africa.
18. B. Spain.

DID YOU KNOW?

The Watergate Scandal was only discovered when security guards in the hotel saw that adhesive tape had been used to hold open doors.

34.
MODERN HISTORY

History is still being made, of course - which, somewhat counterintuitively, brings a book about the past right up to the present day! Although the events outlined in the questions below have all happened in the first two decades of the 21st century, both they and their central figures will no doubt go down in history to come. Cast your mind - to the more recent past!

1. In 2003, which became the first and - to date, only - country to withdraw from the international Treaty on the Non-Proliferation of Nuclear Weapons?

   a. Iran
   b. North Korea
   c. Afghanistan
   d. Kyrgyzstan

2. On what date in 2004 did an immense earthquake trigger a tsunami in the Indian Ocean, leading to the deaths of almost a quarter of a million people worldwide?

   a. New Year's Day
   b. Valentine's Day
   c. Independence Day
   d. Boxing Day

3. In 2005, a woman from Wisconsin became the first person in the world ever to survive what disease without a vaccination?

   a. Rabies
   b. Yellow fever
   c. Japanese encephalitis
   d. Diphtheria

4. Which pope died in 2005?

   a. Benedict XVI
   b. John Paul I
   c. John Paul II
   d. Paul VI

5. What planet was officially downgraded to a dwarf planet by the International Astronomical Union in 2006?

a. Mercury
b. Earth
c. Mars
d. Pluto

6. Which of these technological innovations was introduced in 2007?

   a. Facebook
   b. YouTube
   c. iPhone
   d. Broadband internet

7. In what year did Hurricane Katrina kill over 1,000 people and cause more than $100 billion of damage in the southern United States?

   a. 2002
   b. 2005
   c. 2007
   d. 2010

8. US Airways Flight 1549 safely and successfully ditched in what river on January 15, 2009?

   a. Mississippi
   b. Hudson
   c. St. Lawrence
   d. Ohio

9. True or false: The 33 miners who became stranded underground in Chile in 2010 remained underground for 29 days.

10. In 2011, the southernmost region of what African nation declared its independence, becoming the newest independent nation in the world?

    a. Sudan
    b. Algeria
    c. Ethiopia
    d. Namibia

11. Where was former CIA employee Edward Snowden permitted asylum in 2013?

    a. Norway
    b. Russia
    c. France

d. Greece

12. How many secret documents were made public in the Panama Papers leak in 2016?

    a. 1,150
    b. 115,000
    c. 1.15 million
    d. 11.5 million

13. Which city's Blue Mosque was the subject of a devastating bomb attack in 2016?

    a. Islamabad
    b. Riyadh
    c. Amman
    d. Istanbul

14. In 2017, what viral ransomware cyberattack affected computers in more than 150 different countries?

    a. ILOVEYOU
    b. Graybird
    c. WannaCry
    d. Red October

15. Jacob Zuma resigned as which country's president in 2018?

    a. Zimbabwe
    b. South Africa
    c. Congo
    d. Gabon

16. What famous Parisian building was partly destroyed by fire in 2019?

    a. The Louvre
    b. The Sacre Coeur
    c. The Eiffel Tower
    d. Notre Dame Cathedral

17. In what Middle Eastern port city did an immense accidental explosion of ammonium nitrate occur in 2020?

    a. Beirut

b. Doha

c. Jeddah

d. Kuwait

18. In 2021, it was revealed that which British Prime Minister and his staff had secretly hosted and attended parties in Downing Street, while the rest of the United Kingdom had been forced to obey social distancing rules as part of the strict COVID-19 lockdown regulations?

a. David Cameron

b. Theresa May

c. Boris Johnson

d. Rishi Sunak

SOLUTIONS

1. B. North Korea. The treaty remains in force in 191 other nations.
2. D. Boxing Day. On December 26, 14 different countries suffered loss of life because of the so-called Boxing Day tsunami.
3. A. Rabies.
4. C. John Paul II.
5. D. Pluto.
6. C. iPhone.
7. B. 2005.
8. B. Hudson. Famously piloted by Chesley "Sully" Sullenberger, the flight landed on the water and all 155 people on board were evacuated. The event became known as the "Miracle on the Hudson."
9. False. In fact, they were successfully rescued after 69 days underground!
10. A. Sudan.
11. B. Russia.
12. D. 11.5 million. The documents comprised over two and a half terabytes of computer data.
13. D. Istanbul.
14. C. WannaCry.
15. B. South Africa.
16. D. Notre Dame Cathedral. The fire destroyed the spire and roof of the cathedral, plus melted many of its ancient stained-glass windows.
17. A. Beirut. The explosion killed 218 people.
18. C. Boris Johnson.

DID YOU KNOW?

One of the largest animals to go extinct in the 21st century was the Pyrenean ibex - a type of European wild goat. The final wild individual tragically died in 2000 when it was crushed by a falling tree!

CONCLUSION

And with that final quiz question, our journey through more than 5,000 years of global human history is complete!

From Ancient Egypt to modern politics, you've now faced more than 600 history questions, testing your knowledge of everything from Henry VIII to George Washington's presidency. So how did you fare? Can you still count yourself a true history buff?

Don't worry if you didn't keep track of your score - after 600 or so questions, it can be tricky to keep count! And don't worry if you had to resort to peeking at the solutions along the way here either. Hey, there were some seriously tricky questions in this collection, after all. And even if you did look at the answers, here's hoping you found out some bonus information and a tantalizing background knowledge hiding in there too.

In fact, perhaps after all of this, you're an even bigger history buff than you were at the beginning!

Made in the USA
Monee, IL
09 November 2024

69356445R00134